# THE **ASTRODOME**

# THE **ASTRODOME**

## BUILDING AN AMERICAN SPECTACLE

**JAMES GAST**

ASPINWALL PRESS, BOSTON

Text design by Preston Thomas, www.prestonthomasdesign.com
Printed in the United States of America

The Library of Congress Control Number is 2014944517

ISBN 978-0-9905282-1-0




The Aspinwall Press
P.O. Box 1878
Brookline, Massachusetts 02446

www.astrodomebook.com

Cover Photos:
Top: Historic American Engineering Record (Library of Congress)
Bottom: Darling Photography (George Kirksey Papers, Courtesy of Special Collections,
University of Houston Libraries)

TO THE ARCHITECTS AND ENGINEERS WHO CREATED
THE BIGGEST ROOM IN THE WORLD.

# CONTENTS

A model of Houston's Domed Stadium in 1960 *(George Kirksey Papers, 1910-1971, Courtesy of Special Collections, University of Houston Libraries)*

# PROLOGUE

JUDGE ROY HOFHEINZ HAD GOOD REASON to be confident as he strode into a meeting room at Chicago's Blackstone Hotel on October 17, 1960. His presentation to the National League owners was on the agenda that day, and Hofheinz's colleagues in Houston had been at work for years laying the groundwork for this moment.

Houston, by that time the largest city in the South after years of oil-fueled prosperity, was in the hunt for a major league baseball team. The National League owners—for sixty years an eight-team league—finally seemed ready to deal. Texas represented a new and promising market. The owners were feeling pressure from the rival American League's expansion plans, as well as from the threat of an upstart Continental League being formed in various cities across the country. Offering franchises to two of the Continental ringleaders—one of which was the Houston syndicate Hofheinz was representing—seemed a most effective way to head off that threat.

The deal was almost certainly buttoned up: the other syndicate in contention—New Yorkers seeking to restore a second team to replace the departed Dodgers—were so certain of a favorable outcome they had not deigned to appear in Chicago that day. The Houstonians, however, had been disappointed in the past: Houston baseball deals stretching back nearly a decade had been done, then abruptly undone, and the Houston men were taking no chances. Hofheinz's presentation included a very special hook: an architectural model of a domed stadium.

The model showed a perfectly circular building surrounded by concentric rings of parking. The circular shape itself was somewhat unusual at the time: most ballparks then in existence were on urban sites and the structures tended to take on the irregular geometries of their neighborhoods or of the playing field itself. What was truly remarkable, though, was the glazed roof spanning the entire playing field and surrounding grandstands. The model's roof was removable so the old baseball men could peer inside. They saw round tiers of seats that rose above a perfectly symmetrical baseball field. There were no columns to interfere with the game or the spectators' view. The owners were told that there would be 43,000 seats and air conditioning throughout and that baseball could be played day or night, rain or shine. Construction of the stadium was, of course, contingent on the award of the franchise.

Hofheinz himself was not a man accustomed to taking "no" for an answer. After a hardscrabble childhood, he had graduated from law school at age nineteen, then gone on to election as a Texas state representative, Harris County judge, and most recently, two-term mayor of Houston. Now a prosperous businessman, he had been asked to join the syndicate because he understood infrastructure, politics, construction—and public financing. Brilliant but headstrong, Hofheinz was not a consensus builder; his years in public office and his private business dealings had left a long trail of detractors, but he was known as a person who could get things done.

Although the domed stadium was nothing short of revolutionary at the time, today it is hard to view it as anything other than a necessity. Then as now, baseball season on the Gulf Coast was a sweltering miasma of heat, humidity, and afternoon thunderheads. Houston's minor league baseball team, the Buffalos, had somehow managed to eke out an existence in a small open-air stadium southeast of the city, but from the beginning Hofheinz had insisted that major league baseball would not succeed in Houston's climate.

The National League owners were accustomed to doing business in cooler places. Most of the cities in which their teams played were concentrated in the industrial North. Texas was unfamiliar territory, and Houston had an extreme climate. Listening to Hofheinz, and eyeing the stadium model warily, Milwaukee Braves owner Lou Perini said, "People should pay to go there just to get out of the heat." But Hofheinz's presentation drew a round of applause.[1]

Hofheinz later recalled: "It was the idea of a showplace stadium that sold the majors on Houston."[2]

It is not known just how much influence the novel stadium design had on the owners' decision that day—it was unlikely, league president Warren Giles told reporters, that the exact terms of the deal would ever be made public—but that decision was unanimous. The new franchise was awarded. Houston had made the big leagues, and the domed stadium would become a reality.

## WHY THE ASTRODOME MATTERS

The small drama in Chicago on that day began a forty-year story of a highly unusual and ambitious building that would become known as the Astrodome.

Over those forty years, the Astrodome was the setting for some very compelling stories: Billie Jean King trouncing Bobby Riggs in a legendary 1973 tennis match dubbed "the Battle of the Sexes"; Evel Knievel jumping thirteen cars in 1971; Houston beating UCLA in collegiate basketball's 1968 "Game of the Century"; the Mets edging the Astros in a sixteen-inning Game-7 showdown for the 1986 National League Championship. Even after it was retired as a sports venue, the Astrodome continued to make news as a shelter for thousands left homeless after Hurricane Katrina.

The most compelling story, however, is about the building itself.

The Astrodome is not a distinctive work of architecture. It is certainly not a bad building, nor is it an exceptionally beautiful one. The Astrodome ended its days as a major league venue in 1999, but it remains a uniquely influential building. On the simplest level, it changed the game of baseball and—in the opinion of legions of self-described purists—not for the better. If you happen to be a student of the game, you know that the artificial turf first introduced at the Astrodome changed the way baseball was played, placing a new emphasis on speed and spawning a generation of light-hitting speedsters playing on artificial turf fields with deep fences.

Off the field, the Astrodome's creature comforts and barrage of electronic media forever changed the way the game is viewed. The Dome rose alongside the growing influence of television, and stood as a response to a commercial threat posed by television. To lure paying customers away from their TV sets and into the ballpark, stadiums needed to deliver comfort and amenities on par with the spectators' living rooms. The Dome competed with television by emulating it: a comfortable seat, good food, and frequent electronic distractions. If, while at Phoenix's Chase field, you find yourself engrossed in a video on the 6,200-square-foot high-definition scoreboard while enjoying curried chicken tacos with mint-marinated cucumbers and yogurt on top of scallion pancakes, you can thank—or curse—the Astrodome.

But there is an even bigger story—the tale of building the biggest room in the world, in a time of prosperity and nearly limitless optimism. It is a story that includes the inevitable stumbles, failures, and unintended consequences encountered when building anything that has never been built before. The men who created the Dome had no precedent to consult. As one of them said years later, "[W]e really didn't have any test labs; you can't go look at somebody else's Astrodome and see how they handled it."[3] As a result, the story includes a high-profile design failure—a roof design that made it nearly impossible to play baseball. This problem was overcome swiftly and without any injuries, but not before the Dome became the butt of jokes from sportswriters and late-show talk hosts.

It is the story of an emerging city using its enormous wealth to make its mark, and of America's great migration to the suburbs in search of safety, convenience, and ample parking.

It is also the story of Judge Roy Hofheinz, the Dome's *impresario*. A former county judge and mayor of Houston, a man who cheerfully described himself as a "huckster," a sybarite in a black suit with a fifty-seven-inch waist, Hofheinz not only created the Astrodome but also actually *lived there* with his wife in an impossibly lavish apartment overlooking right field. Many people helped to build the Dome, but it is no exaggeration to say that Hofheinz is the man who got it built.

Most of all, it is a story of American audacity, of building the biggest single room in history in a city with a remarkable tradition of building huge structures in a hurry.

The Dome rose in the early 1960s, alongside the manned space program and its Houston headquarters that was being built at the same time just a few miles away. Like building a rocket thirty stories high and sending it to the moon, the Astrodome was an exercise in innovation—and audacity. Like the NASA scientists and engineers working on the space program, the builders of the Astrodome had to devise solutions for problems that had never existed. Like the problems that cropped up in the space program, the problems of the Astrodome had to be solved under an impossibly tight, self-imposed deadline. And like the space program, the Astrodome came to be because a group of Americans decided it should, and then just went ahead and did it.

PART ONE

# BEFORE THE ASTRODOME

# CHAPTER ONE

# A SHORT HISTORY
# OF BIG ROOMS

A DOME, OF COURSE, WAS NOTHING NEW. To do certain things indoors, you need column-free space. In the world of modern building
design and construction, the term "long span" is generally applied
to structures with spans greater than 100 feet. Beyond that, conventional construction simply will not do. Anything less and you won't
be able to store an airplane, stand in awe of God…or play baseball.

By the time the Astrodome was conceived in the mid-twentieth
century, long spans in the form of domes and vaults had been around
for thousands of years. Until the Industrial Revolution, the spans
themselves hadn't changed much, holding to a range of 140 to 150
feet. The Pantheon (c.125 AD) at 142 feet was the largest dome in the
world for over 1,300 years until construction of the Florence Cathedral (1436 AD), with a diameter of 149 feet. The *Duomo* held on to
the title for over 400 years until the late nineteenth century.*

This slow rate of increase in span was a function of both technology and demand. Before the Modern Era, the role of domes in public
architecture was more or less symbolic, limited to sacred space. Later,
by the nineteenth century, domes were frequently seen atop government buildings such as capitols.

The purpose of these large structures and the vast spaces they enclosed was essentially to awe and inspire, and these structures accomplished that with their height and length. The spans of the Pantheon

---

* Famous domes constructed after the *Duomo*—St Peter's Basilica, St. Paul's Cathedral, and the
U.S. Capitol Building—have shorter interior spans.

The Pantheon (left) and the Florence Cathedral (right) were the largest interior-span domes in the world for over fourteen centuries *(Wikimedia Commons)*.

and the *Duomo* were sufficient for that purpose. Moreover, the materials and technology available to construct domes during these years were limited. The weight of conventional concrete and masonry construction limited the practical span—beyond a certain size a dome simply could not support itself. Simple timber framing weighed less, but its strength was not sufficient for longer spans.

The nineteenth century brought both new technology and new commercial demands. Technology came with the industrial revolution in the form of iron and steel structural framing, which was both light and strong enough to handle the demands of longer spans. Concurrently, new technology in the form of railroads became available to carry long steel members greater distances, and also created a demand for longer spans in the form of vaulted train sheds in passenger stations. Beginning in the mid-1800s, long-span train-shed structures began to creep up well past the 200-foot mark, culminating in 1893 with a 300-foot span at Philadelphia's Broad Street Station.

Around the same time, the rise of international expositions led to another burst of growth in long-span structures, designed for exhibitors from around the world to assemble beneath a single roof to trumpet their technological achievements and display their wares. The

The Crystal Palace, constructed for the Great Exhibition of 1851. A single space so vast it could not be viewed in a single eye span. *(Bridgeman Images)*

first of these was in London in 1851, where Joseph Paxton designed a massive glass-and-iron exhibit hall that became known as the Crystal Palace. At 1,851-by-454 feet,* the sheer scale of this building was dazzling, a single space so vast that it could not be viewed in a single eye span. One visitor reported that "the side walls are too far apart to be embraced in a single glance. Instead of moving from the wall at one end to that of the other, the eye sweeps along an unending perspective which fades into the horizon."[4]

Visitors came in droves, and once inside the great hall, they strolled among exotic goods from around the world—French silks, Russian furs, and an ornate Indian howdah atop a stuffed elephant. They marveled at full-size working examples of the latest technology such as high-capacity printing presses, steam engines, and adding machines.[5] The exhibition was a tremendous popular and financial success, and it achieved its primary purpose of showing off British industrial prowess—including, of course, the building itself.

---

* The length of the building was deliberately set to celebrate the year of the exhibition.

The *Galerie des Machines* at the 1889 Paris International Exposition. Spanning a stunning 364 feet, this remarkable structure was at the time the largest single room in history. This landmark structure was demolished in 1910, but the neighboring Eiffel Tower, constructed for the same exposition, survives.

In the wake of London's success, the great international exhibitions continued to be held every few years in cities around the world. The buildings themselves became attractions, with host nations vying to outdo each other with larger and larger exhibit halls.

About forty years after the construction of the Crystal Palace, this trend culminated at the 1889 Paris International Exposition with the *Galerie des Machines*, an exhibit hall spanning a stunning 364 feet and enclosing over 900,000 square feet, at the time the largest indoor room in history.[6] Just four years later, the Americans seized the record with the Manufactures and Liberal Arts Building for the 1893 World's Columbian Exposition in Chicago at 368 feet—just 3 feet, 10 inches wider than Paris.

As with the classical domes, the purpose of the great exhibition halls was largely symbolic—although the newer structures were commercial, not religious. They were built to promote the technological prowess of industry, and the nations for which they were built. The rooms they shaped were part of the show: they were large not because they had to be but rather because they *could* be.

Then, abruptly, this remarkable wave of construction halted. World's fairs have continued up to the present day, but after the nineteenth century, the large exposition buildings fell from favor. For the

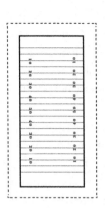
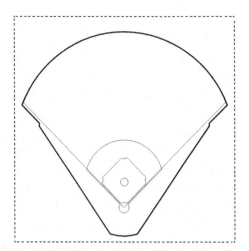

Unlike a football field, which is much longer than it is wide, a baseball playing surface is almost as wide as it is long. *(Illustration by the author)*

newer fairs, planners and exhibitors preferred to construct individual pavilions. The railroads turned against the expense of large train sheds amid the decline of passenger rail service.[7]

The new century brought new technology such as aviation, which led to the construction of large enclosed storage hangars, but both conventional aircraft and even giant dirigibles could be accommodated with smaller spans.* Thus, the structural records established by the great international expositions stood for well over sixty years.

The early 20th century also saw the rise of professional spectator sports that introduced a new functional need for arenas with long spans. However, nineteenth-century spans and building technology readily accommodated major league hockey and basketball, which had been played indoors since their inception. Even football was played indoors for the first time in 1896 at the Chicago Coliseum, a structure that spanned a mere 230 feet. In that game, the University of Chicago edged Michigan 7-6, but the venue itself did not get good reviews. Players and spectators had to contend with dim lighting, and although rain poured outside, a reporter pined for the fresh air and

---

*The Hughes H-4 Hercules "Spruce Goose"—the aircraft with the longest wingspan of any ever built—would have fit handily into either the Paris or Chicago exposition buildings.

even "the sparkling snow" of previous games played outdoors. "Had the day outside been pleasant," he concluded, "the idea of football indoors must have been pronounced a failure."[8] Afterward there had been very few attempts to revive indoor football, and America's gridirons remained open to the sky. Football games, as generations of sodden and frostbitten spectators would attest, were almost never called due to weather.

Baseball, on the other hand, was subject to frequent rainouts, but even by the 1950s it was not possible to play the game indoors. While the great cathedrals, train halls, exhibit buildings, auditoriums and dirigible hangars constructed over two millennia were awe-inspiring feats of engineering, none was large enough to accommodate a regulation baseball game. Baseball needs more space. Unlike a football field, which is much longer than it is wide, a baseball playing surface is almost as wide as it is long. In the middle of the twentieth century, the outfield fences in major league ballparks were placed as far as 460 feet from home plate* and therefore could not fit inside any structure then in existence (nor even in the long-demolished Paris and Chicago exhibition buildings of the previous century).

A structure for indoor baseball with space for thousands of spectators would require an unobstructed span of over 600 feet. That, quite simply, had never been done.

---

* At the time design of the Astrodome began, major league baseball rules required minimum distances from home plate to be 325 feet along the first- and third-base foul lines, and 400 feet to centerfield.

# CHAPTER TWO

# A DOME FOR BROOKLYN

TO THIS DAY, the mention of Ebbets Field evokes gauzy memories of baseball's golden era—a simpler time when fans hopped on city streetcars or walked up busy Bedford Avenue to see their favorite summer game played in a neighborhood ballpark. For many older Brooklynites, hearing the name Walter O'Malley still conjures images of an uncaring businessman, who they believe turned his back on Brooklyn by moving the beloved Dodgers to the sunny skies and fast dollars of California.

That move, however, was not the result of a hasty decision. Before heading west, O'Malley had spent years looking into replacing Ebbets with a new stadium for the Dodgers in Brooklyn.

In O'Malley's opinion, the replacement was long overdue. Ebbets had been constructed in 1913, during a remarkable burst of new stadium construction during the first two decades of the twentieth century. During this time (a period of American history now known as the Progressive Era), the wooden ballparks built in the 1800s were replaced by new structures framed with steel and concrete, and clad in brick. This transformation took place with remarkable speed. In just six years between 1909 and 1915, fifteen new major league ballparks had been opened or completely rebuilt. All were constructed on sites that were readily accessible by public transportation. Many of the ballparks, and the playing fields within, took on irregular shapes to conform to neighborhood streets. In Boston's new Fenway Park, completed in 1912, left field was abruptly truncated to accommodate

Brooklyn's Ebbets Field, opened in 1913. Like many of the Progressive Era ballparks, it remained in use well into the 1950s. *(Author's collection)*

Lansdowne Street. At Ebbets, opened the following year, it was right field that yielded to Bedford Avenue.

This generation of parks hosted thousands of ball games as the United States fought two world wars and endured the Great Depression. By 1950, most of them were still in use; of sixteen major league parks, fourteen had been built before World War I, and they were showing their age. Ebbets, however beloved, was pushing forty years old—more or less the average age of the major league baseball parks in 1950—and was worn out.

These aging venues represented a growing crisis for major league baseball: its stadiums were old, uncomfortable, and sited in declining city centers with no parking. Meanwhile, baseball fans across America were overwhelmingly moving to the suburbs and buying television sets. Attendance at Ebbets was dwindling, and O'Malley placed much of the blame on the ballpark itself. He wanted more comfortable seating, and was irked by the columns that obstructed views of the field. The biggest problem, however was lack of parking. Ebbets, constructed before private automobile ownership became common, had no on-site parking, and space for only a few hundred cars scattered in various small lots in the neighborhood. In the 1950s, a Dodgers fan was more likely to arrive at the park not in a charming streetcar but rather in a private automobile. As parking on the streets of Brooklyn became prohibitive, staying home in Hempstead or Valley Stream and watching the game on television was swiftly becoming a more attractive option.

Since the end of World War II, O'Malley had been looking into a new stadium in Brooklyn to replace Ebbets. He did not consider renovation; he wanted a new facility and a new site, one with room for at least 2,000 parking spaces. Judging by the design and engineering talent he recruited to design his new ballpark, and the elaborate plans they created, O'Malley was serious about keeping his team in Brooklyn—at least at the outset.

The first such studies took place between 1948 and 1952 and were drawn by Norman Bel Geddes, a legendary architectural and industrial designer, a pioneer of *moderne* design whose pen had produced fleets of streamlined automobiles, ocean liners, and air transports. He was perhaps best known for conceiving and executing the visionary Futurama attraction at the 1939 World's Fair in New York. Visitors to Futurama were seated in moving cars that wound their way over and around a model of America in the far-off year of 1960, treated to the spectacle of miniature skyscrapers and automated cars whizzing along highways at speeds over 50 miles per hour.

Bel Geddes's remarkable design for Walter O'Malley's new stadium was first released publicly in 1952. The sketches showed a sleek structure that contained not just a ballpark but also a full-fledged shopping center complete with supermarket, service stations, playgrounds, and a movie theater, all above a 5,000-car parking garage. The site plan was a traffic engineer's dream—dedicated entrances to the garage for private vehicles, multiple parallel curbs dedicated to taxis and buses, all connected to the stadium with grade-separated pedestrian bridges. Inside the ballpark itself, Bel Geddes proposed heated foam-rubber seats, each equipped with an automatic hot dog vending machine (mustard included).

He proposed improvements on the playing field as well. He did not like the quirky dimensions of the existing Progressive Era stadiums, and believed that home-run distances should be standardized.

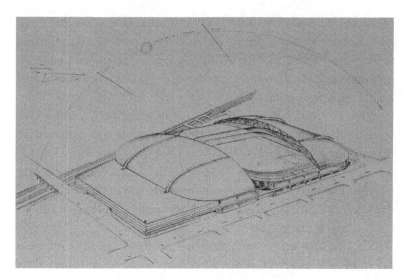

Norman Bel Geddes & Company perspective drawing of an all-weather, all-purpose stadium for the Brooklyn Dodgers, 1949. *(Norman Bel Geddes Theater and Industrial Design Papers, The University of Texas at Austin, Harry Ransom Center; © The Edith Lutyens and Norman Bel Geddes Foundation, Inc.)*

His new stadium would have a perfectly symmetrical playing surface, with uniform distances to the outfield fences. The playing surface itself would have "a synthetic substance to replace grass on the entire field and which can be painted any color."[9]

Perhaps most notably, the plans showed a streamlined retractable roof.

"Spanning the distance of 600 feet is perfectly practical," Bel Geddes told *Collier's* magazine in September 1952, while deftly side-stepping technical questions about the roof technology by saying that such issues would be "a matter for study." Prophetically, the *Collier's* article was titled "Baseball's Answer to TV."

By 1955, O'Malley had, for reasons unknown, dropped Bel Geddes, and was shopping for a new designer. As a replacement, he again went with one of the biggest of names, tapping Buckminster Fuller (known as Bucky to not just his friends but also in textbooks and to generations of architects and engineers). Fuller was every bit as much the visionary futurist as Bel Geddes—and then some. His fertile imagination had produced three-wheeled Dymaxion Cars, prefabricated Dymaxion Houses, Tensigrity structures, and other innovations referred to with catchy syllabic abbreviations. For the most part, these inventions were not commercially successful, but after World War II, Fuller had achieved professional fame largely on the strength of another invention—the geodesic dome.

The word *geodesic* refers to the geometry of the dome's curved surface. The dome is constructed by assembling struts into equilateral triangles (or multiples of triangles), which are joined to form the spherical surface of the dome.* The sides of the triangles align into straight lines that form continuous rings along "great circle" routes. Using the structurally stable triangle (rather than a rectangle) as the basic unit results in a structural shell that is lightweight, strong, and column-free. Fuller had begun experimenting with spherical structures in the late 1940s, and the Cold War brought geodesic domes into prominence in the early 1950s. The lightweight structures were ideal as weathertight covers for rotating radar antennas in the Canadian Arctic for the Distant Early Warning (DEW) line and other military applications.

Having learned about Fuller in a magazine article, O'Malley approached him in May 1955 with a letter describing in great detail his thoughts about how a domed stadium might be designed. The letter closed with a dramatic single-sentence paragraph: "I am not interested in just building another baseball park."[10]

Fuller's plans for the Dodgers, revealed in September 1955, included an aluminum-framed geodesic dome 750 feet in diameter, clad in translucent plastic. The top of the dome would be 350 feet above the playing field. Like Bel Geddes's plans, Fuller's included structured parking below the stadium. A huge model of the facility was constructed by Fuller's architectural students at Princeton and was presented at a press conference. Fuller had calculated the total weight of the structure—one million pounds—but admitted he had no cost estimates. O'Malley bravely told the *New York Times*, "The type of dome Mr. Fuller proposes seems to be quite practical and economical."[11]

The covered stadium was part of a megadeal O'Malley was trying to make with New York City. He had found an ideal site in Brooklyn,

---

* Well-known examples of geodesic domes that remain standing today include the U.S. Pavilion at Expo '67 in Montreal, and the Spaceship Earth Pavilion at Walt Disney World's Epcot.

two miles from Ebbets at the intersection of Atlantic and Flatbush avenues.˙ The site sat at the nexus of no less than nine subway lines, along with a Long Island Rail Road terminal—but O'Malley still wanted his 2,000 parking spaces. He wanted the city to use its eminent domain powers to assemble the property needed for the ballpark. During this period, large tracts of land in inner cities were frequently assembled by eminent domain under federally funded "slum clearance" projects. The property acquired was often turned over to private developers to construct new housing, but in this case it would go to O'Malley, who would build the stadium and an integrated parking structure with private money. The parking would be open to the public when not needed for baseball.

Of course, in the end, O'Malley pulled the Dodgers out of Brooklyn, but over fifty years later his motivation remains in doubt. There are two versions of the story, both of which have some basis in the documentary record. In one, New York City Construction Coordinator Robert Moses was the villain, a role he plays throughout modern urbanist lore. Moses, the story goes, did not like O'Malley, and would not help him assemble the site. O'Malley, unable to overcome Moses's opposition, had no choice but to move west. In a variant of this version, Moses had an additional motive: he wanted the Dodgers as tenants in a new stadium he planned for Flushing Meadows in Queens. This stadium was planned as part of one of Moses's pet projects: a 900-acre park on a site that was better served by the highways that Moses was known to favor.

But the other version of the story is the old one: O'Malley had been wooed by southern California politicians for years, and he wanted to move. He knew Moses would not help assemble the site; even in an era where eminent domain powers were used very liberally, the public purpose of such a venture was dubious at best. In his capacity as city construction coordinator, Moses rarely hesitated to condemn property and call in the wrecking ball, but he was appropriately leery of O'Malley's proposal.[12] Southern California—an enormous untapped baseball market—was simply the better deal. And

---

˙This is the present-day location of Barclays Center, an 18,000-seat multi-purpose arena, constructed in 2012.

it is not unreasonable to assume that O'Malley, however willing to commission elaborate designs for the ballpark of the future, in the end decided that a sunny climate, a conventional stadium, and plenty of at-grade parking was a much safer bet.

This debate has continued for decades, and O'Malley's true thoughts may never be known. There is, however, no doubt about his final decision: the Dodgers moved to Los Angeles for the 1958 season, leaving Brooklyn heartbroken, and the world still without a room large enough for a baseball game.

CHAPTER **THREE**

# A FRONTIER OF SORTS

MEANWHILE, JUST OVER 1,400 MILES TO THE SOUTHWEST, Houston
was vying to make baseball history of its own. Founded in 1836 by
a pair of New York land speculators, Houston at the mid-twentieth
century was still a relatively young city but rapidly outgrowing its antebellum origins as a head-of-navigation port for timber, cotton, and
cattle. After the Civil War, the city had moved aggressively to attract
business to the port around which it had been founded, widening and
deepening its ship channel and adding new railroads to carry goods
between the burgeoning port and the interior of Texas.

By 1901, Houston had shouldered its way past Galveston to become Texas's leading port and was poised to capitalize on that year's
landmark oil strike at Spindletop, just ninety miles away near Beau-
mont. Over the next two decades, more and more oil was found, and
much closer to Houston itself. The Pierce Junction strike of 1920 produced a massive gusher—one that would launch some of Houston's
greatest oil fortunes—just a mile south of what would become the site
of the Astrodome. Houston now found itself sitting on an extraordinary natural resource and with a port in place ready to ship it to the
world. Refineries sprang up near the port and started to line the bayou
east of the city.

During the 1930s, the oil industry began to migrate from its origins in Pennsylvania toward Texas, and Houston. New high rises
began to transform downtown, and opulent mansions sprouted in affluent River Oaks. Houston's population began to swell as thousands
moved into the city to take jobs in the oil industry. At the turn of

the century, Houston had been a city of 45,000. By 1950, oil, World War II manufacturing and annexation had raised the population to 600,000. It was the nation's fastest-growing city.

But the Houston of the early 1950s retained many rough edges. Cattle still grazed a short distance from the high-rise buildings downtown. Gas flares from nearby oil rigs and refineries lit the night sky surrounding the city. As late as 1953, about 500 miles of roads were paved with oyster shell, or not paved at all, and over 5,000 homes did not have indoor plumbing.[13]

Perhaps the roughest edges of all were found in the Jim Crow laws that remained on the books throughout the 1950s. Like all southern cities at mid-century, Houston's public facilities were segregated, with African-Americans restricted to separate and far-from-equal parks, schools, libraries, and stadiums. All or most of the unpaved roads and outhouses were in their neighborhoods. African-American baseball fans who bought tickets to see the minor league Houston Buffalos play at Buff Stadium were consigned to shadeless bleachers and separate restrooms. It was the law of the land, not just in Texas but across the entire South, in a broad arc that reached from El Paso to the shores of the Potomac River in Virginia, just across the river from the Lincoln Memorial.* It was part of a national tragedy, and it was about to change.

Even though it was the nation's fastest-growing city, Houston also had the dubious distinction of being the largest city in America with no major league sports team.

It was not for lack of trying. In 1950, oil wildcatter Glenn McCarthy[†] had proposed an enclosed football stadium with seating for 75,000 to 100,000 spectators on land he owned near the present-day site of the Astrodome. He'd taken the design to a meeting with team owners of the National American Football League (later the National Football League), but his bid for an NFL franchise was turned down.[14]

---

* The Pentagon, designed in the early 1940s in compliance with Virginia law, was constructed with segregated washrooms. However, during construction in 1941, an executive order banning discrimination in federal facilities was signed by President Roosevelt, and the "colored" and "white" signs were never placed on the doors.

† The previous year, McCarthy opened the Shamrock Hotel, which was boldly sited five miles from downtown Houston, the first major building outside the city center. McCarthy and his hotel are perhaps best remembered for their fictionalized roles in Edna Ferber's epic novel Giant. In the 1955 film version, the McCarthy character was played by James Dean.

The men who brought baseball to Houston at Colt Stadium in 1962. Left to right: Robert E. "Bob" Smith, Judge Roy Hofheinz, George Kirksey, and Craig Cullinan were the key members of the Houston Sports Association. At the rear is Paul Richards, who joined the organization as general manager in 1961. Just four years after this photo was taken, only Hofheinz remained; the other four had left or were pushed aside. *(George Kirksey Papers, 1910-1971, Courtesy of Special Collections, University of Houston Libraries)*

High school and college football was indeed popular in Texas, but like the rest of the country, pro football had not yet caught on. The big game remained baseball.

During the time that Walter O'Malley was pondering his enclosed stadium for the Dodgers, four men were coming together in an epic effort to bring major league baseball to Houston. The founder of this group was George Kirksey, a former sportswriter turned public relations man who advocated for baseball virtually from the time he arrived in Houston in 1946. A native of North Texas at a time that baseball, not football, was the biggest sport in the state, Kirksey had been a UPI baseball writer in the interwar years. He had covered fourteen World Series, had worked in New York alongside Damon Runyon and Grantland Rice and—perhaps more propitiously—in hotel restaurants and bar rooms across the country, expertly bending an elbow alongside major league ballplayers and front-office men. Although a difficult man to get along with, Kirksey knew baseball, baseball men, and the business of baseball. He viewed Houston's minor-league status as a personal affront. Recalling those early days, he later said, "I always resented the fact that in the *New York Times*, the *Chicago Tribune*, the *San Francisco Chronicle* and other leading papers in the United States they have a baseball calendar where they list the standings in the major league clubs and to see Houston listed as a Minor League team, a Minor League city."[15]

Kirksey had a small public relations firm that, while not lucrative, provided inroads into Houston's business community. He had been trying to get a ball club in Houston throughout the 1950s, hoping to take advantage of opportunities presented as old-line baseball franchises started to relocate. He assembled investors and made a bid to purchase the St. Louis Cardinals but lost out to brewery magnate August A. Busch. He moved on to talks with the Reds, Cubs, and White Sox, hoping to lure those teams to Texas, only to see each potential deal evaporate.

As a one-man show of modest means and minimal diplomatic skills, Kirksey was astute enough to recognize that his modest PR practice, his enthusiasm, and his baseball cronies were not sufficient to do the job. Attracting a major league team would take a more organized approach, the support of Houston's business community, and plenty of cash. Kirksey needed a partner with enough clout to marshal those resources.

Reaching out to his business contacts, he was introduced to thirty-one-year-old Craig Cullinan, grandson of the founder of the Texas Company (later Texaco). Like Kirksey, Cullinan was a native Texan, but also a product of Phillips Andover and Yale. By Houston standards, Cullinan represented "old money," and he provided connections to Houston's boardrooms and monied families. It was Cullinan who had the personal credibility and connections to convene Houston's captains of industry in a spacious bank boardroom in January 1957 for the founding of the Houston Sports Association. Formation of the HSA marked the beginning of a concerted and moderately funded effort to attract the major leagues to Houston.

Joining forces, Kirksey and Cullinan traveled to every major league city, making overtures to the elite fraternity of ballclub owners informally known as "the Lodge." At the outset, they spent most of their energy trying to convince some of those owners to move their existing teams to Houston. It was a daunting task. Baseball teams might relocate from time to time, but for the most part they stuck with the established industrial cities of the North and East. In the mid-1950s, Kansas City represented baseball's most remote southwestern outpost.

They found themselves in a classic "chicken or egg" situation: baseball teams would not really take them seriously without a major league stadium, but at the same time back in Houston they could not garner much interest in funding a stadium without an actual team in hand.

Kirksey pushed Harris County's political leadership to fund a stadium. He frequently cited the success of major league baseball in Milwaukee when the Boston Braves moved to a county-funded stadium in that city in 1953. Today, public funding of sports stadiums is routine, but in the 1950s it was a relatively new phenomenon. Moreover, Texas law at the time forbade counties from issuing revenue bonds for that purpose.

The latter obstacle was quickly overcome by Kirksey's relationship with Searcy Bracewell, a former client who had gone on to become a state senator. In 1957, Bracewell, who also happened to be a skilled lobbyist, pushed through legislation enabling certain counties to issue bonds and oversee stadium construction. As required by the legislation, a Harris County Board of Park Commissioners was formed to oversee construction.[16] This paved the way for a July, 1958 referendum in which Harris County voters authorized a $20 million ($162 million in current dollars, which in this book reflects year 2013 values[17]) bond issue. This vote marked the first of a series of referendums, spanning a period of fifty-five years, in which voters were asked to fund the county sports stadium.

With the bond issue passed, the county park board started searching for a site and interviewing architects to design what was then envisioned as an open stadium. They devised a concept for a rounded triangular stadium with movable stands that could be used for both football and baseball. It was the first time anyone had tried to create such a facility from the ground up.[18]

Kirksey and Cullinan, now armed with a rudimentary stadium plan for which funding was in hand, continued their visits to major league owners but remained unable to dislodge an existing team. They moved on to an expansion strategy, hoping to convince the Lodge to add teams and to locate one of them in Houston. At the outset, that was an extremely ambitious goal. In those days of low-paid players who were barred from bargaining for themselves, baseball was a more profitable business than it is today, and the owners were not inclined to share their lucrative pie, nor were they willing to dilute the quality of their talent pool of players. No new team had been added to either league since 1901.

Meanwhile, other cities were getting into the major-league hunt and had joined forces to form a new Continental League, which became one of the more intriguing chapters in the history of major league baseball. The new league was a consortium of minor-league cities (Minneapolis, Denver, Buffalo) led by a powerful New York syndicate that was seeking a team to replace the recently departed Dodgers and Giants. In 1957, Kirksey reached out to the New Yorkers, and Houston became one of the nascent league's primary members when it was formally established in 1959.

The Continental League members tried diplomacy first, imploring the American and National league owners to add new teams to their schedules. Rebuffed, the Continentals turned to hardball tactics by challenging the 1922 federal antitrust exemption that Major League Baseball had used to enforce a virtual monopoly on player talent. The Continentals prevailed on influential members of the U.S. Senate to sponsor a bill eliminating the exemption, and in the summer of 1960—with the support of the Senate's powerful majority leader, Lyndon Johnson—the bill came very close to passing. For the major league owners, this was a near-death experience, and a clear signal that The Lodge would have to come to the negotiating table and work with the upstarts. Within a few months, the two existing leagues finally agreed to add teams, and Houston was considered an odds-on favorite to get one of them.

As the Continental League took shape and gained influence, Cullinan and Kirksey sought additional capital for their prospective Houston franchise, having learned in their travels that even deeper pockets would be needed to fund a major-league team. That brought R.E. "Bob" Smith into the picture.

Born to a struggling prospector and oilman in 1894, Smith had himself started out as an oilfield roughneck. He had risen through the rough-and-tumble world of Texas wildcatters and amassed one of the many small fortunes that marked Texas in that era. He had shrewdly invested his earnings in land in the rural areas surrounding Houston. At the time he was approached to join HSA, Smith was the largest landowner in Harris County and a *very* wealthy man. Smith's civic influence and deep pockets were greatly coveted by HSA, and Kirksey made great efforts to bring him into the fold, in one case angling for an introduction by engineering an opportunity for a "chance" meeting with Smith while visiting a mutual friend in the hospital.[19]

A former semiprofessional ballplayer himself* Smith was interested in joining the effort and attracting a team. Like the others who

---

* In the prewar days, many Texas companies and even municipalities fielded baseball teams that played in highly competitive local and regional leagues. The team rosters were stocked with employees who were frequently recruited for their baseball talent and paid under the pretense of menial or no-show jobs.

came before him, Smith knew his limitations. He purchased land as an investment; for the most part he did not develop his own property. He brought significant financial weight to the consortium but was not well versed in development, infrastructure, or government relations. For those matters he had relied on a business partner for several years, and now he insisted that that partner join the effort.

That brought Judge Roy Hofheinz into the picture.

# CHAPTER FOUR

# THE JUDGE

*Interviewer: Did you get along with Roy Hofheinz?*
*Astrodome architect S.I. Morris: You don't have to get*
*along with him. You just have to say "yes."*[20]

HOFHEINZ IS THE SINGLE MOST INSTRUMENTAL FIGURE in the
Astrodome story: a politician and rags-to-riches businessman who
blended the steely vision of Robert Moses with the opulent tastes and
showmanship of Elvis Presley. He was a man of extraordinary intellect, energy, and eloquence. Hofheinz could instantly master complex
technical subjects and speak about them as if he were a seasoned expert. A mesmerizing and persuasive speaker, he could hold audiences
of any size spellbound. He may be best remembered for his theatrical
instincts, inviting comparisons to Cecil B. DeMille, who was his favorite director,[21] or P.T. Barnum, whose circus he would purchase a
few years after the Astrodome was constructed. He was a headstrong
and slightly eccentric visionary, and by his own cheerful description
a "huckster."

He inspired tremendous loyalty in his friends and colleagues. In
interviews conducted more than thirty years after his death, those
who knew and worked for him speak of him with genuine affection
and uniformly praise his kindness and compassion, along with his
intellect and energy. But in life, he certainly was not loved by all: his
high-profile career in both the public and private sectors left a long
trail of detractors and hard feelings. He was incapable of turning the

Judge Roy Hofheinz at the Astrodome. *(RGD0006, Houston Public Library, HMRC).*

other cheek and never seemed to embrace the often-false bonhomie that marks the most successful politicians. He was intolerant of persons he felt were not up to his intellectual standards and scornful of subordinates who lost his confidence.[22]

Hofheinz was the type of person who lies at the center of any successful large-scale public construction project. First and foremost, he was uncompromising. There was no good reason to do anything in any other way but his way. He was autocratic and just slightly eccentric. Perhaps most important, he was capable of masterminding the broadest strategy as well as commanding its tiniest detail and placing his personal imprint upon both. Hofheinz conceived the Astrodome and expertly managed the strategic picture, steering it through the shoal waters of politics, finance, and public opinion—all while finding the time to personally tend to the most minute details such as selection of china and silverware for the stadium's restaurants.

Above all, Hofheinz was a promoter and a salesman. His overwhelmingly favorable 1980 biography, penned by his friend the newspaperman Edgar W. Ray, is titled *The Grand Huckster*. His seaside home on Galveston Bay was called Huckster House.

Huckster House was filled with eccentric touches and opulent oddities. Visitors were visually bombarded by a succession of exotic themes, and every room had a name: the Harem Room, the Gay Nineties Room, the Buccaneer Room, and the South Seas Lodge. Hofheinz was a circus aficionado, so there were also several tributes to the Big Top: a Circus Room, a genuine circus calliope, and a drinking fountain fashioned as a lion's head. Thirsty guests had to stick their heads inside the lion's mouth to get a drink. In later years, Hofheinz would bring a similar, even more lavish touch to his private suite in the Astrodome and would maintain that the gaudy touches were intended to serve as sales tools by leaving a strong impression on visitors. That may indeed have been the case—his salesman's instincts were impeccable—but it was more likely the man was just having fun.

He almost always had a big cigar, and in fact it is difficult to find a photograph of him in which he is without an eight-inch-long Sans Souci Perfecto, lit or unlit. He claimed to smoke, chew, or otherwise consume two dozen a day.

He was not one to write memos; in fact, he rarely signed documents and avoided written communications in general. "A lifetime habit," his son Fred recalled. "Never put anything in writing."[23] He would instead summon aides for meetings at all hours of the night, or call them, preferably on one of the gold telephones he used in his private-sector offices. A year of research among thousands of archival pages spanning years of Astrodome design and construction produced no internal memoranda from him and just three letters bearing his signature. These letters provide a neat cross-section of Hofheinz's tale during the first year after opening the Dome. Two are perfunctory thank-you notes: one to President Johnson for attending opening night, and the other to one of many citizens who wrote in with a suggestion about correcting glare problems with the Astrodome roof.

The third is a one-page letter firing HSA founder George Kirksey, carefully preserved with Kirksey's papers. Hofheinz was not one to let sentiment get in the way of power.

Perhaps most memorably, Hofheinz was a lifelong big eater with an enormous waistline, a characteristic reporters almost never failed to mention. While a state legislator in Austin, he once surprised a dinner companion by telling the waiter to bring his dessert first. He attributed his immense appetite to a hardscrabble childhood. According to his son Fred, he overate because "when he was younger, there wasn't anything to eat; he had to support his mother. His father died when he was a very young guy. They struggled to feed themselves. Ever since then if he got his hands on food, he'd eat it."[24] From time to time he would go on diets, but that ended as Hofheinz approached age fifty, and his girth only ballooned thereafter.

Despite his spartan childhood—or perhaps because of it—his life and career were characterized by remarkable determination and unparalleled success. Nearly every profile of Hofheinz written over the past fifty years has included a recitation of his precocity: he entered law school at age seventeen and passed the bar at nineteen. He was elected a state legislator at twenty-two, county judge at twenty-four, and mayor of Houston at forty.

However, young Roy Hofheinz actually demonstrated his considerable talents even earlier. The son of a laundry-truck driver, Roy arrived in Houston with his family in 1923 at the age of eleven. As a four-teen-year-old San Jacinto High School student, he showed considerable entrepreneurial skills by producing and promoting large dances for teenagers (modeled on such events for adults, which were very popular at the time). The dances were huge affairs with multiple orchestras that lasted until the wee hours. Roy somehow found the up-front money to book the halls and the bands, then sold tickets, kept a watchful eye out for alcohol and misbehavior, and swept up afterward.

Roy showed his flair for showmanship in his promotion of the events in school, in newspaper ads, and with his Ford Model T, which he would drive about the streets of Houston decorated with red and white advertising placards. On at least one afternoon before a big dance, the jalopy "broke down" at one of the city's busiest intersections. Hofheinz removed one of the wheels, propped it alongside the car, and then stood nearby for much of the day, politely declining all offers of help and garnering maximum exposure for the advertising plastered on the sides. Hofheinz's biographer Edgar Ray describes Roy's promotion of a "Yo-Yo Dance": dressed in a clown suit, he fashioned an enormous yo-yo out of two trash-can lids, then positioned himself as a barker at a busy corner in front of the Gulf Building downtown, holding a rein on a billy goat.[25] It was, to say the least, memorable, and that was one of his most important sales tactics throughout his life.

The teenager also branched out into media, convincing the *Houston Chronicle* to buy his high school sports stories at ten cents per column inch. He also produced a weekly amateur hour on local station KTLC, for which he purchased the radio airtime, recruited the talent, sold the advertising, and emceed.

In 1928, Roy's father's laundry truck was struck by a car in Houston's Heights neighborhood. Fritz Hofheinz died three days later, making Roy, just out of high school at age sixteen,* head of the household. He had won scholarships to attend the University of Texas in Austin, but he did not want to move over 150 miles away from his now-widowed mother. Instead, he enrolled at Rice Institute (now Rice University) so that he could stay at home with her. By that time,

---

*Public education in Houston at that time ended at Grade 11.

he was already becoming a successful entrepreneur. He continued to promote and stage dances, expanding his market east from Houston as far as Lake Charles, Louisiana. The 1930 Federal Census shows Roy and his mother living on Francis Street in Houston and lists the eighteen-year-old's occupation as "advertiser."[26]

Rice, then as now, was a top-tier school, but classes were held during the day—not good for Roy's array of growing businesses. He withdrew and enrolled in night classes at Houston Junior College and later entered Houston Law School. While still in school, he went to court for permission to sit for the bar exam (normally administered only to those twenty-one and over), and passed it at the age of nineteen. In 1931, he established his own law practice while still in law school.

At the age of twenty-two, Roy was ready to move into politics, which had interested him for years. Back in 1928, the Democratic National Convention had been held in Houston, and the sixteen-year-old had talked his way onto the floor as a page for the New York delegation. There he met nineteen-year old Lyndon B. Johnson, another ambitious Texan who at the time was a student at Southwest Texas State in San Marcos.[27] This was the start of a long political relationship, and as will be seen, LBJ went on to make several appearances in the Astrodome story.

Hofheinz and LBJ were cut from the same political cloth. Both were stalwart Democrats:* Roosevelt men, New Dealers, populist, and attentive to African- and Mexican-Americans. Johnson aide Jack Valenti recalled that the two were "remarkably similar men in their drive, ambitions, absorption of facts, and in their massive and almost occult powers over those with whom they came in contact."[28] Hofheinz would go on to manage southeast Texas for Johnson's 1941 and 1948 Senate campaigns.[29]

The hall in which Hofheinz and Johnson first met foreshadowed future Houston can-do construction achievements. Once the Democrats agreed to hold their 1928 convention in the city, Sam Houston Hall was constructed in just sixty-four working days. The structure covered nearly six acres and an entire city block on Bagby Street[†]

---

* Texas, like most Southern states, was consistently Democratic until the 1970s.
† In 2014, the Hobby Center for the Performing Arts stands on this site.

Once the Democrats agreed to hold their 1928 Convention in Houston, Sam Houston Hall was constructed in just sixty-four working days. The roof vault (shown under construction at top) was framed with the Lamella system, proprietary structural technology that would again be selected for the great Astrodome roof thirty-three years later. (*MSS0100 and MSS0056, Houston Public Library, HMRC*)

and was built of one million board-feet of yellow pine, an abundant and readily obtained material from the vast forests of East Texas and neighboring Louisiana. This wood-framed hall with a seating capacity of 16,000 persons was sited next to a large fire station, which was probably not a coincidence. The main convention floor was 272 by 326 feet and covered by three vaulted roof segments, the largest of which was 120 feet wide. The roof vault was framed with the Lamella

system, proprietary structural technology[30] that would again be selected for the great Astrodome roof thirty-three years later.

Hofheinz's own political career was marked by a meteoric rise and
corresponding setbacks. He was elected to the state legislature at age
twenty-two in 1934 and then quickly moved on to a more powerful
post as Harris County judge in 1936. Under Texas law, the county
judge is essentially the "mayor" of the county: he is its head adminis-
trator and budgeting officer, presides over its governing body (called
the commissioner's court), and serves as judge of the county court.
Hofheinz served two terms in this influential post, devoting much of
his energy to infrastructure improvements. He replaced oyster-shell
roads,* built two toll-free tunnels beneath the ship channel, supported highways to Galveston and Ft. Worth, and led a new county
flood-control district. Perhaps the best-known legacy of this chapter
in Hofheinz's political career was the title itself: although he later became mayor of Houston, for the rest of his life Hofheinz was referred
to as "the Judge."

In 1945, at the age of thirty-two, Hofheinz completed his third
term as judge and moved to the private sector. Upon leaving office, he
said he would use his time in private life to make money,[31] and for the
next eight years, he diligently made good on that promise. He built
a fortune in construction materials, broadcasting, and real estate. He
acquired radio stations in Houston, the Rio Grande Valley, and Al-
abama, then branched into television, then in its infancy, joining a
syndicate that acquired one of Houston's earliest TV stations.

By 1952, he was ready to return to politics, and was eyeing the
mayor's office. The incumbent was Oscar Holcombe, who had first
been elected in 1921 and had served twenty (non-consecutive) years
as mayor. It was Holcombe who welcomed the Democratic delegates
to the 1928 Convention in the great pine hall. As the 1952 election
approached, Mayor Holcombe was hobbled by charges of cronyism
and viewed as perhaps a little out of touch.

Hofheinz had made it known he was interested in becoming
mayor, and was invited to a meeting with Houston's influential
business leaders. These men were collectively referred to as the "8-F

---

* Along the Gulf Coast, crushed oyster shell was frequently used in lieu of gravel to pave rural roads.

Group," after the corner suite in the Lamar Hotel where they regularly met to lunch, play poker, and chart Houston's future. Hofheinz made a favorable impression, and was poised to benefit when the incumbent stumbled. Holcombe purchased fifteen minutes of television time for a campaign appearance, but unfortunately the time slot he selected bumped that night's episode of *I Love Lucy*. This was a deadly error for any American politician in 1952, and the television station's switchboard was flooded with angry calls.[32] Shortly afterward, the 8-F Group threw its support to Hofheinz, who won the election the following November.

The "kingmakers" who had tapped Hofheinz to run for mayor did so because he had been a very successful businessman. Fred Hofheinz recalled, "They thought he was one of them."[33] They soon learned otherwise, as the new mayor indicated that he was not inclined to take direction from the fiscal conservatives in Suite 8-F. Telling them "I'm the one that's got elected,"[34] he proposed a ten-year, $500 million ($4.3 billion) capital improvement program and a 20 percent property tax increase.

Hofheinz's two terms as mayor were marked by extraordinary acrimony. Idealistic and impatient, he quickly developed a highly confrontational relationship with the city council. He publicly referred to several council members as "cookie-jar boys," linking them to the reputed cronyism and petty corruption of the previous administration. Unsurprisingly, the "cookie-jar boys" did not take kindly to this nickname or its implications, however true. Relations deteriorated from that point on. When several councilors refused to appear for a meeting called by Hofheinz, the mayor ordered the police chief to track them down and arrest them. The political tumult reached a crescendo in 1955, when Hofheinz was impeached by the council. Hofheinz dealt with this setback by ignoring it: he refused to yield power or vacate his office, locking himself in with his staff.

Amidst the tumult, Hofheinz could claim genuine accomplishments. He continued to advocate for roadway and infrastructure improvements, and he is remembered for playing a discreet role in integrating Houston's municipal facilities. He desegregated City Hall, the libraries, and even the public golf courses. He accomplished this not

by preaching or pleading: instead, with a stroke of a pen, he simply ordered the WHITES ONLY signs removed. Recognizing the sensibilities
of the times, he called in newsmen and convinced them not to report
the changes. These tactics were effective. While there were pockets
of opposition from city employees, the facilities were peacefully integrated, and the stage was set for desegregation of Houston's privately
owned facilities about ten years later. At least partly as a result of these
efforts, Hofheinz maintained steady support from African-American
voters, a key voting bloc that would come into play in financing the
Astrodome in the following decade.

But the constant clashes with the city council had taken their
toll, and Hofheinz was under political siege as he entered his third
year as mayor. In a risky attempt to break the logjam in his favor, he
sponsored a special charter amendment, under which all of the city's
elected officials would be recalled—including the mayor.

Hofheinz's gambit failed. The establishment abandoned him, and
selected a candidate to run against him—Oscar Holcombe, the man
he had replaced in 1952. In the November, 1955 special election campaign, Hofheinz did not go quietly; his public statements took on a
decidedly populist tone, and he began to rail against the 8-F crowd,
calling them "fat cats" who ran Houston behind the scenes. But after
three years, voters had had enough, and Hofheinz was soundly de-
feated by Oscar Holcombe.

During his tenure as mayor, Hofheinz had been considered a prospect for governor, but losing the mayoral election removed that as a
possibility. Hofheinz was cast into the political wilderness and never
held another elected post.

After leaving office in 1955, Hofheinz resumed his profitable life
in the private sector, focusing on broadcasting and real estate. He
formed a partnership with his longtime friend and supporter R.E.
"Bob" Smith, and they collaborated on land speculation and development amid the mushrooming suburbs surrounding Houston.
Like any land speculators, they sought to acquire property in the
path of development. Upon leaving City Hall in 1955, Hofheinz had
shrewdly hired away his chief land planners, men intimately familiar
with where roads and other infrastructure were planned. S.I. Morris
recalled that during this period Hofheinz "was working in planning

to take advantage of the expansion opportunities that were available in real estate in Houston by protecting Smith's properties in such a way that they would get the sewer and the water and the road systems they needed."[35]

Smith was by that time the largest landowner in Harris County but typically did not develop his properties; he held the land for investment purposes. "I have a thorough belief in inflation," Smith said, presciently, in the days just before the Great Inflation of the 1960s and 1970s. "That's why I invest in land."[36]

Hofheinz, however, wanted to build. During the 1950s, regional shopping centers were starting to appear in suburban areas throughout the country, as more Americans were moving away from inner cities and farther from downtown retailers. During this period, a trend-within-a-trend emerged in the shopping mall. In this new building type, the storefronts were turned inward to face each other across a central pedestrian walkway, which in the earliest malls was open to the sun and sky. Houston's first mall, the Gulfgate Shopping Center, opened in 1956. As mayor, Hofheinz had turned the first spade of earth at Gulfgate's groundbreaking ceremony, and now he took notice of its great success.

Gulfgate was east of downtown Houston, on the highway to Galveston. The geographic and population center of Houston, however, was moving west. Smith's vast land holdings were focused on this largely rural area, and Hofheinz owned an eighty-acre homestead there as well. In 1958, they pooled some of their holdings into a 100-acre tract off Yorktown between San Felipe and Westheimer and proposed a massive new mixed-use project under the working title of Smith-Hofheinz Shopping City. As usual, Hofheinz was thinking big: the initial phase of the project was to include over a million square feet of retail, and 7,000 parking spaces, figures that would have eclipsed the entire inventory of existing retail space in downtown Houston. Most notably, the stores were to be linked by a 1,600-foot-long, fully enclosed and air-conditioned mall.[37]

At the outset, Hofheinz had hired a well-known shopping center architect* to design the new project, but before long a geodesic dome

---

* Seattle-based John Graham Co., designer of the Gulfgate project as well as Northgate Center near Seattle, the country's first regional mall.

caught his eye, and he sought out the man credited with its design—
R. Buckminster Fuller.* A meeting was arranged, and Hofheinz and
Bucky "hit it off beautifully," leading to lengthy discussions about
a domed shopping center.[38] In later years, Hofheinz liked to say,
"Buckminster Fuller convinced me that it was possible to cover any
size space if you didn't run out of money."

The Shopping City project, however, never made it past the planning stages. Developer Frank Sharp was also advancing a large shopping center for his Sharpstown development less than four miles from
the Smith-Hofheinz site. Sharp was the first to land Foley's Department Store—a major "anchor" tenant essential to the viability of any
large shopping center, enclosed or otherwise. Feeling that the market would not support two regional shopping centers so close to each
other, Hofheinz and Smith eventually dropped their plans.

But the Shopping City project and his brief collaboration with
Buckminster Fuller had sparked Hofheinz's imagination. Years later,
Fred Hofheinz would recall that air conditioning and domes "stuck
in my dad's mind,"[39] and those ideas would come into play when
Hofheinz became involved in the campaign to bring major league
baseball to Houston.

Hofheinz was forty-seven years old when George Kirksey and
Craig Cullinan approached him in the summer of 1959, and invited
him to join HSA. The Judge was enlisted largely because of Bob
Smith's growing investments in, and influence with, the syndicate.
Smith wanted him involved, and Kirksey and Cullinan hoped that
Hofheinz would use his influence with Smith to increase his invest-
ment, and to make his land on South Main available for the stadium.

Hofheinz did indeed have Smith's ear, but he brought other skills
to the table. By virtue of his years as an elected official, Hofheinz
had a solid grasp on planning, financing, and construction of public
facilities, and he gradually assumed a leadership position regarding

---

* Prototypes of Fuller's invention were displayed at a number of locations around the world
in the 1950s. Fred Hofheinz recalled that his father saw a geodesic dome at an exposition in
Montreal sometime around this period. Hofheinz may have seen a proposal for "Shoppersville," a Fuller-inspired domed shopping center that was being planned in Montreal in 1958.
Shoppersville would have been centered around a 525-foot diameter aluminum geodesic dome.
The project was never built. ["Domed Shop Area to Rise in Canada," *The New York Times* May
25, 1958; Fred Hofheinz, interview by the author, Houston, August 30, 2013]

the construction of the stadium. Cullinan and Kirksey had no such experience, and they gladly allowed this to happen.[40]

In the short term, they were wise to bring Hofheinz into their consortium, as he brought important experience they lacked. In the long term, their decision doomed them, as Hofheinz would rapidly elbow his way to leadership of the HSA. Then, as he consolidated his power, some of the others stepped aside. Others were pushed. Within a year of the opening of the Astrodome, Cullinan, Smith, and Kirksey would all be gone, and Hofheinz would stand alone as its master.

PART TWO

# DESIGNING A DOME

CHAPTER **FIVE**

# A MEETING AT BRANDT STREET

ON A SUMMER EVENING IN 1960, Seth I. Morris, a forty-six-year-old architect known to everyone as Si, was summoned to a meeting at Hofheinz's Brandt Street office. Now that the Judge had taken over as HSA's stadium overseer, he was Morris's primary client contact. Morris and his colleagues would soon grow used to such after-hours summons. The Judge worked very long hours and needed little sleep. He often hatched new ideas late at night and routinely called subordinates at all hours to discuss them.*

Si Morris and his business partner Talbott Wilson were high school and college classmates. Both had attended architectural school at Rice Institute, and the two had started an architectural practice in Houston in 1938. Theirs was one of two firms that had been hired in 1958 by the county Board of Park Commissioners to design the new stadium.

Morris and Wilson came to the park board interview with a portfolio that was largely single-family residential, private clubs, apartments, and college dormitories. The private-club work had proven to be particularly valuable in terms of connections for the young firm; as Morris later said, "When you build a club, you get to know a lot of people who run things."[41] While their firm was very highly regarded

---

* In an interview that appeared in the April 9, 1990, *Houston Post*, architect Robert Minchew recalled an episode after the Astrodome opened: he was awoken by a call from Hofheinz and summoned to the office. He found the Judge leading a conversation about whether hot dog relish could be dispensed from squeeze bottles. The group adjourned at 3:00 A.M., having determined that it probably wouldn't work.

Architect S.I. Morris *(RGD0005, Houston Public Library, HMRC)*

in Houston,* at the time Morris and Wilson had no experience with athletic facilities, and very little with large-scale projects. They had, however, designed a home for park board chairman William Kirkland, and it is likely that relationship got them in the door. During the interview, lacking more substantial athletic credentials, Morris and Wilson felt compelled to cite their experience as second-string in-fielders for their high school baseball team.[42] Whatever weight the board gave this argument is unknown, but Morris Wilson Crain and Anderson was selected to share the commission with Lloyd and Morgan, another local firm.

Hermon Lloyd and William Morgan were also Rice graduates, and they had a few more large projects under their belt. Along with some downtown office buildings, they were veterans of a landmark

---

* The firm, now known as Morris Architects, remains highly regarded, and is still headquartered in Houston.

Completed just hours before hosting its first game in 1950, the new 70,000-seat Rice Stadium was designed and constructed in eleven months. *(RGD0006, Houston Public Library, HMRC)*

Houston-area project—Rice Stadium, which had been completed in 1950 after an epic undertaking. Rice, at the time a nationally ranked football powerhouse, had previously played its home games in a 32,000-seat stadium. In those days, Rice football was the biggest game in town, and there was increasing interest in a new stadium. In November 1949, George Brown, executive vice president of Texas-based contractor Brown & Root (and a Suite 8-F regular), announced that the project would move forward, and that his firm would build the new stadium at cost. As if that civic gesture were not enough, Brown gave himself and his team 11 months to complete the project—two months for design and nine for construction. Ground was broken on January 3, 1950, and crews worked double 10-hour shifts through the following months. Time was so precious that the contractors resorted to casting concrete columns using formwork left over from the recently completed Gulf Freeway project. In an often-quoted anecdote that may be apocryphal, George Brown was asked if the stadium would be finished in time for Rice's home opener in September. Brown is said to have replied to the question with another question: "Is it a day or night game?"

The massive 70,000-seat facility was indeed completed in September 1950, just hours before kickoff of the first game of the season (as it turned out, a night game).

The scale, and speedy construction of Rice Stadium was a reminder of Sam Houston Hall a generation before, and a precursor to the Astrodome, which would follow ten years later. It was the sort of feat that characterized Houston at mid-century—evidence of, in the words of one of the Astrodome architects, "the affirmative, why-the-hell-not attitude of a metropolitan area that was still a frontier of sorts."[43]

Now, eight years after Rice Stadium was completed, Lloyd and Morgan had joined forces with Wilson, Morris, Crain & Anderson for the purposes of the new stadium project. The two firms referred to their joint venture as "The Associated Architects." It is worth noting that the two primary architectural firms were based in Houston, and they designed the Astrodome with minimal reliance on imported talent from what were then the major centers of architectural design on the East Coast and Chicago. With very few exceptions, the architects and engineers who designed the Dome were native Texans who had received their architectural training at Rice.

Lloyd and Morgan won a coin toss to determine which firm's name would be listed first, and the Associated Architects got to work. For the first two years, the project did not progress very far; most of the efforts were centered around a site-selection study led by Morris,* with little or no work done on the stadium itself.

Now, as Morris approached the big house on Brandt Street that summer evening in 1960, there was a greater sense of urgency. The Continental League was becoming a reality, and Houston's prospects to land a team were improving dramatically. With Hofheinz taking the reins, the pace of the project began to quicken.

Hofheinz maintained multiple offices throughout the city; his real estate interests were based not in a high-rise but in a gracious house on

---

* See Chapter 10.

Brandt Street south of downtown.* His office was lavishly decorated with antiques—tall, handcrafted brass chairs with velvet cushions; a Louis XIV desk; and, in what would become one of Hofheinz's recurring interior-decoration themes, an adjoining washroom with gilded fixtures, including the toilet seat.[44]

The meeting attendees that evening included Morris's joint-venture colleagues Wilson and Lloyd, and county Judge Bill Elliott. Once the meeting itself was under way, Hofheinz shared his thoughts on the new stadium. He told the group that Houstonians could not be expected to attend ball games in the hot sun amid high humidity and mosquitos. He went on to say that he had been impressed by the geodesic domes being designed by Buckminster Fuller, who had told him that a stadium for 65,000 people could be fully enclosed with a dome. Hofheinz had decided that the new stadium in Houston would be covered, air-conditioned, and have natural grass.

Then came the challenge: Hofheinz said that he was amenable to working with the Associated Architects, who had been hired by the park commission two years earlier. But he wanted to hear what the architects thought about the dome idea. Blindsided, Morris initially tried to dodge the question, but Hofheinz drilled in: "Well, if you don't think you can do it, I'm going to hire Buckminster Fuller."

Morris, whose experience at that time was largely in residential buildings,[†] was now very much on the spot. If he declined to meet Hofheinz's challenge, he could lose the commission—or perhaps keep it but be forced to work under Fuller. For most architects, the latter prospect, a client-mandated shotgun marriage with a "big name" architect from out of town, would be as distasteful as losing the job entirely, if not more so. Morris, a fiercely competitive businessman, had to make a quick decision.

"Hell, we'll do it!" he blurted out.[45]

Morris acted boldly that night. He almost certainly did not know just how he and his colleagues would deliver such an unprecedented

---

* This house still stands, having narrowly escaped demolition during construction of US-59 in the early 1960s. It has been carefully restored by its current owners, who operate it as Hofheinz House.
† In subsequent years, Morris went on to a highly respected career that included large-scale commercial and civic projects in Houston as well as across the country.

project. But then, no one really knew. Previously, the idea of a covered stadium had been the subject of occasional wishful thinking. Hofheinz's decision put an end to that—both the political leadership and the design team were now committed to building a domed stadium in Houston. The project was announced in the press on August 21, 1960.[46]

While there is no doubt that Hofheinz was responsible for championing the enclosed stadium in Houston, the source of the idea itself is murkier and has been obscured by legend. For years, Hofheinz repeatedly said he had been inspired by a visit to the Colosseum in Rome. He said that he had been intrigued to learn that it had a retractable canvas sunshade, called a *velarium*, which could be pulled over the top of the stadium to protect spectators from rain and sun. This story was frequently repeated by the Judge and his publicists (the inaugural-year program *Inside the Astrodome* includes a grandiose two-page spread that meticulously compares the statistics of the two structures, with the Astrodome edging out its elder on nearly every measure). This appealing and memorable tale has long worked its way into the printed record and is at least partially true; as mayor, Hofheinz did visit Rome with the World Congress of Mayors, and it is reasonable to assume that he would have toured the Colosseum during that trip.[47]

But did Hofheinz truly have his covered-stadium epiphany amid the ruins of ancient Rome? Hofheinz's son Fred firmly believes that his father was inspired by a modern domed project elsewhere.[*] Moreover, it is clear that Walter O'Malley was not just the first to advocate a domed stadium, but he was also the first to cite the Colosseum as a precedent.[†] It is more likely that the Shopping City project sparked Hofheinz's interest in spanning and air-conditioning large spaces.

---

[*] See Chapter 4.

[†] O'Malley cited the Colosseum during a 1955 press conference announcing the Dodgers' covered-stadium project. Robert Moses needled O'Malley about this comparison in a letter written the following year: "There may have been a translucent roof over the original Colosseum, but if you succeed in getting one built over the [Brooklyn] Sports Stadium, your fans will always refer to it as 'Walter O'Malley's Translucent Dome.'" [Roger Kahn, "Will Travel for Stadium," New York Times, June 11, 2005; and Robert Moses, letter to Walter O'Malley, Dec. 6, 1956. http://www.walteromalley.com/docu_detail.php?gallery=1&set=11&docuID=68&pageNum=1; accessed November 28, 2013.]

Years later, architect Ralph Anderson, with characteristic blunt-ness, told the Judge's biographer: "There have been many stories about where Hofheinz got the idea for the Dome. There are those who attribute the idea to his having seen the Colosseum in Rome or to some kind of brain washing he was given by Buckminster Fuller on the geodesic dome...I think Hofheinz will have to be the final authority on the real genesis."[48]

Whatever the provenance of the idea itself, Hofheinz owned it from that point forward. He ordered up a model of the domed sta-dium, and that was the model he brought to the October, 1960 meet-ing with the National League owners at Chicago's Blackstone Hotel.

# CHAPTER SIX

# GOING TO THE POLLS

IN THE WAKE OF ITS GREAT TRIUMPH IN CHICAGO, the HSA set an aggressive schedule to construct the new stadium they had shown to the National League owners. As 1960 drew to a close, the plan was to break ground in February 1961 and have the stadium completed by March 1962, in time for the new franchise's first home game. This schedule, likely inspired by the Rice Stadium saga, was highly ambitious even by Houston standards. No matter—Cullinan told reporters that drawings for the new domed stadium were "virtually completed," while Kirksey confidently told reporters that construction would go quickly because Houston had "two advantages and those are terrain and climate."[49]

The true state of the schedule was sobering. Cullinan's claim about "virtually completed" drawings was a bit of a whopper: the design work at that point had barely started, and the construction documents not at all. Hofheinz's slick model belied a project in an early stage of design and with many unresolved issues.

Moreover, the project's financing was not yet settled. A domed stadium would of course be more expensive than a conventional one, and Hofheinz wanted to change the project's financing from the revenue bonds approved in 1958 to tax-backed general obligation bonds with lower interest. This would require another county-wide bond referendum, which was hastily scheduled for January 1961.

Publicly funded professional sports venues are now a routine fact of political life, but in 1961 there were relatively few such facilities. The referendum faced organized opposition from persons opposed to the use of public funds for what they viewed as a private enterprise. They derided the project as "the doomed stadium." Some of the opponents were the very "fat cats" Hofheinz had taunted during his mayoral years.

Winning over the voters would take a political campaign, and Hofheinz ran it as one, making speeches, holding rallies, and sending sound trucks through neighborhoods urging voters to the polls. He established a blue-chip citizens committee favoring a "yes" vote, co-chaired by Leon Jaworski, president of the Chamber of Commerce and an influential Houston attorney who went on to greater fame as Watergate special prosecutor in 1973.

As Jaworski worked Houston's boardrooms and business establishment, Hofheinz turned to another key political bloc. In his previous campaigns, Hofheinz had paid great attention to African-American voters, and now he reached out to that community again for support with the bond referendum.

The election came during a pivotal time for civil rights in Houston. At the same time Hofheinz was convincing architects and politicians to build a revolutionary domed stadium, Houston's Jim Crow policies were slowly giving way. The city's lunch counters had been integrated over a few months in 1960. This had been sparked by sit-ins and peaceful student protests, but it was ultimately accomplished by quiet maneuvering behind the scenes. In a remarkable three-way collaboration, moderate white business leaders secured agreements from supermarkets, drugstores, and restaurants to integrate. Then one day in August, by mutual arrangement, African-Americans appeared without fanfare, sat down at the lunch counters, and were served. Also by agreement, none of this had been reported in local newspapers, radio, or television. To avoid inflaming segregationists, Houston's media agreed to a self-imposed blackout. It was the same tactic used by Mayor Hofheinz when he had integrated city facilities a few years earlier, and it was effective.

To secure African-American support for the 1961 Bond election, Hofheinz reached out to Quentin Mease, a key leader in that community. With Hofheinz seeking political support, Mease saw an opportunity to dispose of another segregationist barrier. He agreed to campaign for African-American votes on the condition that seating, dining and washrooms in the new stadium would be fully integrated. Hofheinz and Bob Smith agreed.[50]

Hofheinz would later say that he "had a colored policy and the policy was 'green.' If you had the green you could get through the gate."[51]

These efforts paid off, as Election Day turnout was high, and the $22 million ($171.4 million) referendum passed by a solid margin. African-American neighborhoods overwhelmingly supported the measure, offsetting opposition in many rural and suburban areas. Monitoring election returns from Brandt Street, Hofheinz jubilantly announced that "dirt will fly on South Main immediately."[52]

Before any dirt could fly, however, the project's opponents bounced back. A lawsuit challenging the bond issue halted the project for nearly three months, essentially ending hopes of completing the new stadium in time for the start of the 1962 baseball season. The opening date was postponed one year to 1963—still a very ambitious schedule—and plans were made to construct a temporary outdoor stadium so that the new team could host games while the domed stadium was under construction.

During this hiatus, the Associated Architects did not have a contract in place to do their work. The HSA paid to keep some activities moving; however, then as now, architects faced with an interesting or high-profile project have a surprising tendency to work at risk (and at times for free), and that is exactly what they did during this period.*

While the Astrodome would become known for some lavish interior finishes, the building itself was a taxpayer-funded public works project with a strict budget of $15 million ($117 million). Speaking with reporters in February 1961, Hofheinz refused to consider the possibility of a cost overrun. "We're building a $15 million stadium," Hofheinz said. "...and that's the figure we're sticking with," said county judge Bill Elliott.[53]

But there was a long road ahead, and that budget turned out to be not so strict after all.

---

* The Associated Architects worked without a contract until receiving a letter of intent in June 1961, and did not receive a signed contract until November of that year.

# CHAPTER SEVEN

# ASSEMBLING A DOME

*"Well, it was scary. But we weren't doing anything really
new. Everything we did had been done before; it just
hadn't been done to that scale."*
— ARCHITECT S.I. MORRIS[54]

THE TIME HAD COME to turn the concept shown in Hofheinz's model
into reality, and the architects began work on the Dome's *construction
documents*, the detailed plans and specifications used by contractors to
build the building.

The principals of the two firms divvied up the work according to
their specialties and expertise. Talbott Wilson and Hermon Lloyd collaborated on architectural design. William Morgan was, in Morris's
words, "the specification guy," charged with technical matters and
preparation of the construction documents. Morris's partner Ralph
Anderson was given what became the most fateful task of all—getting
the roof to work and getting the grass to grow inside.* Morris himself
became the front man, a role he later described as "a PR job,"[55] handling the designers' relations with the client, the government agencies,
and the contractors. He would later recall, "I spent most of my time
keeping everybody calm."[56]

Any large building is like a puzzle consisting of hundreds of
thousands of pieces—concrete, steel, glass, ductwork, and electrical

---
* See Chapter 8.

conduit—that must be assembled. Sometimes the pieces have con-
flicting agendas, operating at functional cross-purposes. At other
times, the puzzle pieces simply will not physically fit together, and the
design must be modified. In this regard, the Astrodome was like any
large building.

But the architects and engineers who would create the biggest
room in the world would face even greater, unprecedented challenges.
First, they would have to find a way to place a roof above the big
room, then they would have to manage the environment inside.

## THE ROOF STRUCTURE

The roof, of course, was the Dome's reason for being. It was there to
keep bad weather out and a comfortable environment within. Since
there could be no columns on the playing field or in the stands, it
would need a clear span of well over 600 feet, and no dome of that size
had ever been built before.

Surveying the industry in late 1960, the Associated Architects
found several structural technologies that could produce such a span,
and a number of engineers, fabricators, and contractors who specialized in such structures. These firms were in the business of designing and building familiar long-span public buildings—auditoriums,
gymnasiums, and churches—as well as more utilitarian projects such
as aircraft hangars and large fuel tanks. The architects began discussions with these firms in late 1960, soon after the National League
franchise was awarded.

Initially, the architects planned to procure the roof as a *design-build*
contract. Under this arrangement, somewhat unusual at that time, design and construction of a building (or in this case, a portion of a building) is delegated to a single firm that is responsible for both design and
construction. This approach is often used for highly specialized types
of construction, and the AA's interest in this route belied the architects'
trepidation about taking on the unprecedented engineering challenge.
The rest of the stadium was to be of more conventional construction
and would be procured via the traditional *design-bid-build* process, in
which the designer and contractor are separate.

At the time design work began on the Astrodome, the Union Tank Car dome in Baton Rouge, Louisiana, was believed to be the largest interior span dome in the world. This industrial facility housed an ingenious turntable system that simplified maintenance of freight-rail tank cars beneath a dome spanning 384 feet. *(Photo by Alfred E. Gebhardt, courtesy of Anthony Bianchi.)*

Over the winter of 1960–61, the Associated Architects obtained preliminary design-build roof proposals and estimates from several firms. Buckminster Fuller remained in the picture; although Hofheinz did not carry through on his threat to hire Fuller directly, it appears that he wanted to keep Bucky involved.[57] Synergetics, a North Carolina firm founded by Fuller* and subsequently turned over to a small group of his protégés, was one of those engaged in the design-build discussions. They had just completed the Union Tank Car dome in Baton Rouge, Louisiana, which was believed to be the largest interior span dome in the world at that time.† For Houston, they proposed an aluminum-framed geodesic dome.

---

\* Fuller held the patent for the geodesic dome. Although frequently referred to as an architect, Fuller was not trained or licensed to practice architecture. He therefore relied on licensed professionals to seal construction drawings. Although Hofheinz met at least once with Fuller, all correspondence with the AA regarding geodesic domes was with Synergetics.

† The Centre des Nouvelles Industries et Technologies in Paris, completed in 1958, is a triangular, concrete shell structure that spans 715 feet along each side. It was, and remains a remarkable feat of engineering, but it is not a dome, and the space within is not large enough to hold a baseball game.

The other proposers offered a wide variety of technologies: air-supported structures, cantilevered trusses, and geodesic domes. Perhaps the most remarkable came from Oregon-based Timber Structures, Inc., which proposed to build the enormous dome out of structural timber. The company produced a drawing showing its approach, which would have been quite a sight had it been built: the huge roof would have been framed with laminated timber trusses, with members 11 inches wide by 42 inches deep, fastened together with huge steel gusset plates the size of tabletops.[58]

None of the companies that sent in proposals seemed fazed by the scale of the project. The span that would be needed for the dome in Houston was unprecedented. But as Si Morris had observed, existing structural technology could readily be scaled up to meet it. And as Buckminster Fuller had observed, someone was willing to pay for it.

The architects gave their closest consideration to two choices: Fuller's geodesic dome and the lamella system. In the selection process, the geodesic dome lost ground quickly—after gathering estimates from the various proposers, the AA found it was among the most costly systems. While in later years Hofheinz would make frequent references to his discussions with Buckminster Fuller, the geodesic dome was dropped from active consideration by June 1961. This marked the end of Fuller's participation, however indirect, in the Astrodome project, although Bucky would remain a distant observer and would offer up a few choice opinions in later years.

The lamella system is a close cousin of Fuller's geodesic dome. Both capitalize on the structural principle of *triangulation*. Invented in Germany in 1908, a lamella roof comprises a large number of inter-connecting timber or—in the case of the Astrodome—steel members forming a diamond-shaped pattern. The term *lamella*, trademarked at the time the Astrodome was designed, refers to the lozenge or diamond shape of the structural bays. Like a geodesic dome, the numerous lamella units mutually brace each other at frequent intervals, so the stress is evenly distributed.[59] Properly detailed, a lamella roof is very beautiful, with the structural members forming a graceful pattern of elongated diamonds across a curved surface.

For the Associated Architects, the true beauty of the lamella system may have been that it could be fabricated using standard structural steel shapes, unlike the geodesic dome, which would have been constructed of custom-fabricated aluminum rods and connections. Public agencies—and the Dome was a public project—generally do not allow specifying a single proprietary product. It is difficult to obtain exceptions for such policies, and the architects would have been eager to avoid that headache.[60]

Like Fuller's geodesic dome, the lamella system was a patented technology, with only a handful of engineering firms licensed to use it. One of those firms was Roof Structures, Inc., of St. Louis, a company that had designed lamella domes in timber and steel across the United States. The company's founder and senior engineer was German-born G.R. Kiewitt, who specialized in lamella structures. The Associated Architects hired his firm as a consultant in June 1961, making Kiewitt, who was a practicing architect as well as an engineer, the man responsible for the great roof.

While the tremendous span would become one of the Astrodome's great technological achievements, selection of the structural system turned out to be one of the project's most promptly resolved design issues—it took about six months to sort through a wide range of options and make a selection. This allowed the designers to move on to managing the environment within the dome, and a new array of challenges that were not resolved quite so easily.

## BENEATH THE DOME

Typically, managing the environment inside a building means controlling noise, lighting, temperature, and humidity for human comfort. In a conventional building, these factors are strongly interrelated, and sometimes they become competing interests. The biggest room in the world would need to do all these things while also providing a suitable place to grow more than two acres of grass.

At the outset, the architects envisioned a dome whose roof structure would be visible from the exterior. Ideally, the structure would be exposed, with the roof surface itself suspended below. This approach exploited the visual drama of the complex structures, and was seen in many of the other dome projects (such as the Union Tank Car Dome, see previous photo) that were sprouting up around the country during the period. Early models and drawings of the Astrodome depict a fully glazed roof framed in a diamond pattern to match the lamella truss below. This was certainly the preference of the architects, whose modernist training and sensibilities would have led them to express the building's structure on the exterior.

The architects were quickly convinced otherwise by their acoustical consultants, Massachusetts-based Bolt Baranek and Newman (BBN). Any domed or vaulted space will reflect and focus sound in unexpected and undesirable ways: a normal conversation, even a whisper, on one side of a domed space may be heard with great clarity on the other. This phenomenon can be readily experienced in buildings such as the U.S. Capitol, and Grand Central Terminal, where tour guides use this "whispering gallery effect" to entertain visitors.

London's Royal Albert Hall offers a story that in many ways foreshadowed that of the Astrodome. Completed in 1871, it was constructed with an elliptical glass dome spanning 185 by 217 feet—believed to be the largest dome in existence at that time. After the building was occupied, it became apparent that the dome's shape and hard glass surface produced exceptionally poor acoustics. The problem was so acute that a canvas awning was added beneath the dome. The canvas absorbed some sound, and had the added advantage of protecting the occupants from rare London sunshine. In 1949, the glass of the inner dome was removed and replaced by sound-absorbent material, and engineers would continue to tinker with acoustical treatments for the building throughout the twentieth century.[61]

In addition to the inherently poor acoustic performance of a hard dome, the acoustic consultants also pointed out that a plastic dome surface would produce an almost intolerable level of noise during a rainstorm.[62] It soon became clear that from an acoustical standpoint, a fully glazed roof would be a disaster.

Still, it was understood that there had to be enough glazed area to admit sunlight so that the grass would grow, and while BBN would have preferred to cover the entire dome with sound-absorbing material, a series of compromises were explored: a grid of acoustic baffles hung below the plastic dome, and "factory-type" clerestory skylights with acoustical treatment on the underside.[63]

The final decision was to treat the roof as a lattice, or grid, in which half of the overall roof area was opaque with acoustic treatment, with the remaining area directly over the playing field "perforated" by skylights. The shape and pattern of the skylights was the subject of many design studies and discussions. For visual reasons, the architects experimented with circular and diamond-shaped skylights set in patterns that would be geometrically compatible with the diamond-shaped lamella bays within. In the end, these staggered layouts lost out because they would interfere with water flow off of the huge roof in heavy rain, and the designers chose to play it safe with a layout of rectangular skylights set end to end, and parallel within each 15-degree segment of the dome. This arrangement was at best a compromise, and was at the time a disappointment to the architects, who were troubled by the series of awkward, arrowhead-like forms running along each 15-degree segment.[64]

All told, from a design standpoint, the Dome's roof was a disappointing series of compromises. After the original dramatic design concepts, technical and financial constraints had overcome an opportunity for distinctive architecture. But any regrets about lost architectural opportunities were soon set aside in the interest of dealing with greater challenges.

## 4,596 SKYLIGHTS

As the structural and architectural design of the great domed roof began to gel, various details of the roof design presented another array of unknowns. The decision to use individual skylights—the final total was 4,596 individual units—in an otherwise solid roof led to concern about what players would see when they looked up. The architects feared that the alternating pattern of dark ceiling and bright sky would prove too distracting a background when tracking baseballs or footballs in flight above. During the fall of 1961, they made elaborate

This 1964 construction photo shows the rectangular lattice of skylights and acoustical material against the diamond-shaped pattern of the lamella superstructure. It was an awkward visual relationship but the architects had few options. *(Elliott Papers, Harris County Archives. Photo by Peter Whitney, courtesy of Mike McCorkle)*

plans for a full-scale simulation in a World War II–era blimp hanger at the former Hitchcock Naval Air Station near Houston. A section of the highest portion of the hangar roof—approximately the height of the proposed domed stadium—was to be perforated with large rectangular holes and covered with polyethylene film, approximating the size, spacing, and transparency of the skylights planned for the roof. The plan was to bring Colt ballplayers to field fly balls "to determine whether a problem exists either from a height or visibility comfort point of view."[65]

There is no record of the test having taken place,* perhaps because the blimp hangar suffered major damage during Hurricane Carla the same month, and most of the building was demolished in 1962. Whatever the reason, it was a missed opportunity for a preview of what would become a big problem later on.

The architects also recognized that there would be a related problem with shadows. The network of diagonal lamella trusses overlaid with

---

* Tal Smith, when interviewed in 2013, was confident that it did not take place.

the matrix of rectangular skylights would cast harsh, complex shadows on the field. The shadows would have been visually distracting, and would have unevenly distributed precious sunlight on the grass.*

For this reason, the architects designed *diffusers* into each skylight. Diffusers are commonly used to reduce glare and hard shadows from a bright source of light and spread it evenly throughout an area. The simplest example of a diffuser is a lampshade. More sophisticated diffusers are found in larger buildings. The ceiling-mounted light fixtures found in many office buildings use *prismatic* diffusers—plastic sheets hung horizontally below the lamps and embossed with a myriad of tiny prisms. These diffusers scatter light very efficiently over large areas, and are also effective at reducing glare when viewed from the side—an important advantage in large, open office areas and one that the designers wanted to take advantage of in the Dome. Because most spectators would view the great roof from an acute angle, prismatic diffusers would improve their comfort.[66]

"There will never be a shadow in the stadium," Hofheinz said a few months before the Dome opened,[67] and he was right, although problems would become evident later.

The Dome's designers had very effectively juggled a number of technical issues with their roof design: structure, sound control, shadows, and precious sunlight for the grass.

Unfortunately, they had not considered every angle of their unprecedented design. They somehow failed to anticipate how the complex overhead structure and diffused sunlight from 4,596 individual skylights would appear when viewed from directly below—as they would be seen, for example, by an outfielder.

## BASEBALL'S ONLY AIR-COOLED STADIUM

For the new stadium in Houston, cooling had been on everyone's mind from day one. In 1958, soon after the stadium design contract was awarded, and well before Hofheinz transformed the project into a dome, George Kirksey instructed the architects that "air-cooling

---

* The potential problems with shadows would later be demonstrated in construction photos taken after the roof structure was erected but before the skylights were added; a distracting lattice of shadows overlay the entire field.

should have a top priority" for what was then to be an open stadium. Kirksey cited the success of a Carrier cooling system installed in the dugouts at Cincinnati's Crosley Field, and underscored his point by stating, "We would like to advertise; 'Baseball's only air-cooled stadium.'"[68] As it turned out, the architects and engineers would be spared the challenge of air conditioning an open stadium, but plenty of technical hurdles remained.

Modern air conditioning had been invented in 1902, and by 1960 the technology was mature. Air conditioning a building of the Dome's size was becoming routine. In fact, there were already larger buildings with air conditioning. The Pentagon, completed in 1943 with a gross floor area of over six million square feet, was fully air-conditioned. Houston's new Domed Stadium would have a mere 400,000 square feet of floor area. However, there was an important difference between these two large buildings: unlike the thousands of individual rooms within the Pentagon, most of the Dome would be a single room of approximately 41 million cubic feet. Moreover, that single room would place great demands on a cooling system—a humid subtropical climate outside, a glazed roof that would admit solar energy from above, and nearly 50,000 human spectators who would generate heat merely by being there. Even the grass would generate heat.

As is typical for most building projects, the architects hired mechanical engineers as consultants. All of the architects knew Israel A. Naman, a mechanical engineer who had had his own Houston practice since 1947. By 1960, it was the largest such practice in Houston, and Naman was recognized as an authority on air conditioning. Like most of the design team, Naman had been raised in Texas and was a Rice graduate. The Associated Architects hired Naman as a consultant to design the heating, ventilating, and air conditioning (HVAC) system for the new stadium.*

As Naman began his work in 1961, he had to come to grips with several huge challenges created by the sheer volume of the space.

The first challenge: a single room over 200 feet high. The height of the space would result in *stratification*: since heat would naturally

_____
* A second mechanical engineering firm, Dale Cooper & Associates, was also brought on to design the building's central plant, and plumbing system.

rise inside the huge space, temperatures would vary widely between the lowest and highest levels. Without proper air control, temperatures could be oppressively high on the upper levels, even as people on lower levels shivered. Naman solved this problem by dividing the space horizontally into three air-conditioning zones, and designing a separate air handling system for each zone. This made it possible to deliver air at different temperatures to each level, and even to cool the upper level while heating the lowest.

The second big challenge was *distribution* of the cooled air. Nearly all modern buildings have some form of ductwork that delivers air from a central plant to the spaces that need heating or cooling. This air is sent through ducts and delivered through outlets (such as grilles) in the individual room, and must be pushed from the outlet to reach the entire space and its occupants. The distance that the air must be pushed within each room is called *throw*. Most homes and office spaces require a throw of only a few feet. Larger spaces, such as auditoriums or movie theaters, require longer throws—at the time, perhaps up to 100 feet. In these conventional spaces, the problem can be simplified by adding outlets in the ceiling and floors.

In the Dome, however, overhead ductwork could not be used—it would be unsightly and could block sunlight, views of the field, and even batted balls. All of the air would have to be delivered from the perimeter, so keeping the big room cool would require throws of well over 300 feet to cover both the spectators and the playing field. Keeping the field cool was not so much about the comfort of the players: the Dome was intended to host conventions and events such as boxing matches, where the public would gather on the field. While that was feasible, it would be all too easy to aim wrong. Aim too high and cool air would fly right over the spectators and chill the players; aim too low and the opposite would be the case.

Naman addressed this problem by working with manufacturers to develop registers with throws of over 350 feet. These were placed in clusters of four nozzles around the lower balcony that would blow out in various directions toward the playing field. Naman wisely built plenty of flexibility into his design—he made the nozzles adjustable, and used a combination of automatic and manual temperature controls. This kept his engineering options open by allowing final adjustments to take place after construction was complete. Months later, as the building neared completion, he was able to set each set of nozzles independently, using smoke bombs to track where the air was thrown.

## GO AHEAD AND SMOKE

Dealing with throw, Naman later recalled, was the easy part. For him, the greatest challenge of all had to do with one of America's favorite pastimes—which, in this case, was not baseball but rather smoking.

When design of the Dome began in earnest, the landmark 1964 Surgeon General's Report was over three years away, and 70 million Americans—roughly 40 percent of the population—were regular to-bacco users.[69] Smoking was permitted almost everywhere in America, including theaters, airports, and of course stadiums. Applying these demographics to the seating capacity of the Dome meant that up to 20,000 persons would reasonably be expected to light up at some point during the game.

The issue was not so much about protecting nonsmokers: given the sensibilities of the early 1960s, there would be few scolds with the temerity to complain about smoking. However, managing the smoke was critical to the success of the design, because too much smoke in the air would affect everyone in the stadium, whether they were smoking or not. Pyridine, a byproduct of cigarette smoke, burns the eyes. Conventional filters would not remove it, and changing the air more frequently would add expense.* The solution was to recirculate the air through activated charcoal filters, a technology used for gas masks. It would take ten boxcars worth of charcoal to handle the volume.

With the pyridine removed, you would at least be able to keep your eyes open during the game. But now the question became: would you be able to see anything through all the smoke? To watch

---

* Most mechanical building ventilation systems are designed to continuously exhaust stale air and replace it with fresh air from outside. In most mechanically ventilated buildings the air is changed several times every hour. Air brought in from the outside must be heated or cooled to the interior temperature. In very cold or very warm climates, frequent air changes can become costly.

1965 advertisement in *Architectural Record*. American Air Filter Company manufactured the electrostatic precipitators that were used to filter tobacco smoke in the Dome. *(Author's collection; reprinted with permission of AAF)*

a baseball game, you frequently need to watch a baseball, and that means maintaining visibility adequate to see an object just 3 inches in diameter from up to 700 feet away. Moreover, as the smoke becomes more dense, you would begin to lose color rendition, and start to see shades of gray.

There was no realistic means of getting rid of *all* the smoke. The problem couldn't be solved simply by changing the air more often; in those days, so many people were smokers that even in outdoor stadiums a smoke cloud would normally be seen over the stands. The smoke could be managed using electrostatic precipitators, but that was expensive. So the question became: how much smoke could remain while maintaining enough visibility to see the game?

In one of the scientific-style experiments that would be used to design the Dome, Naman set up an apparatus that pumped cigarette smoke into a box with glass on two sides and an optical instrument that would determine the density of the smoke in terms of a 700-foot viewing distance. On one side of the box was a screen showing a color movie of a baseball game. When you looked through the other side, you were watching the game through smoke, at varying densities.

How much smoke was too much? This would be a key design criterion, and Naman wisely did not make this critical call on his own. He convened a group, including the architects and Judge Hofheinz, to sit in a room and watch ball game movies through his contraption. The amount of smoke was gradually increased until the acceptable limit was determined by consensus.

Finally, Naman devised a way to exhaust the remaining smoke and stale air up through a huge cupola set in the apex of the dome. The opening was so large that Naman feared high winds would actually draw air out of the building. That in turn would have reduced the air pressure inside enough to prevent the exit doors—which must always swing out for safety—from being opened in an emergency. So he had emergency buttons installed next to the exit doors that would shut dampers in the cupola and allow the doors to swing freely. Fortunately, this elaborate system was never needed.

Naman was proud of the work he did at the Astrodome, and rightly so. He came to grips with questions that had never arisen, and he innovated effective engineering solutions that would keep thousands of people cool, comfortable, and able to enjoy a clear view of the game, along with a cigarette or two.

The toughest customers, however, would need more attention.

# CHAPTER EIGHT

# THE GRASS

WHILE KEEPING 45,000 HUMANS COMFORTABLE was, of course, a high priority, the most formidable challenge was in looking after the welfare of the Dome's other living inhabitants: *Cynodon dactylon,* known familiarly as Bermuda turfgrass. The great dome would have to span the largest room in the world, but it would also have to admit enough sunlight for grass to grow. This issue would consume a re-markable share of the design team's attention over the following years. In the end, it proved to be the Astrodome's Achilles heel, the cause of a high-profile design failure.

The task of getting the grass and roof to work in harmony fell to architect Ralph Anderson, Jr., thirty-seven years old at the time that he began work on the Domed Stadium. Anderson was a Houston native, son of a sportswriter, and—like most of his colleagues on the domed stadium project—a graduate of Rice Institute.

Anderson was a talented architect and a tenacious individual. Upon graduating in 1943, he was inducted into the Army and sent to Europe. Among Anderson's archived papers at Rice, alongside his striking architectural sketches and drawings, is a GI-issue helmet pierced by a single bullet hole. Anderson was wearing the helmet at the time the bullet struck during the Battle of the Bulge. He received the Purple Heart for his injury (from which he fully recovered).[70]

On the Dome project, Anderson was working in uncharted terri-tory, for no one had ever tried to grow two acres of grass indoors. This requirement created one of the Dome's great quandaries. Grass, of course, needs light to grow, so it would benefit from larger skylights

Architect Ralph Anderson was responsible for getting the roof and the grass to work in harmony. *(Ralph Anderson, Jr. Papers, 1860–1989, MS 413, Woodson Research Center, Fondren Library, Rice University)*

that would act like a greenhouse. However, larger skylights would reduce the area available for acoustic absorption while also increasing solar gain, thereby taxing the air conditioning system. It was a case of clashing priorities on a grand scale.

In the beginning, Anderson tried to find a way around this technical challenge by using artificial grass. The problem was, at that time, such a product did not exist. During the winter of 1960–61, he canvassed manufacturers of synthetics: Union Carbide, 3M, Dow Chemical, U.S. Rubber, and Dupont. Anderson also reached out to carpet manufacturers. While a few of the companies reported that they were tinkering with ideas for artificial turf, none had a suitable product ready for market.

The architects even tried to invent artificial grass of their own, preparing a sketch showing hexagonal tiles of rubber with inset tufts of plastic. They sent the drawing to a few manufacturers, but couldn't interest anyone in producing it.

But even if artificial turf had been available at the start, there were strong feelings that it might represent too much innovation. Soon

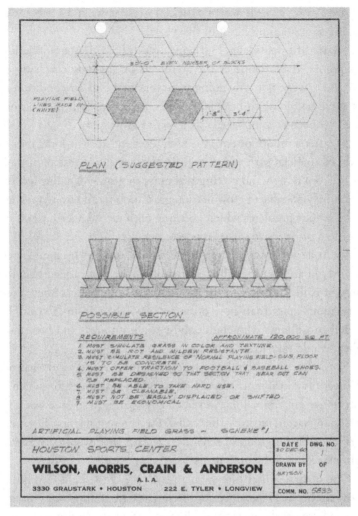

Hoping to garner industry interest in producing a product that did not yet exist, the architects prepared this 1960 sketch concept for "Artificial Playing Field Grass." (*Robert J. Minchew Houston Astrodome Architectural and Engineering Collection, 1928-1990, Dolph Briscoe Center for American History, The University of Texas at Austin.*)

after the Astrodome opened, Hofheinz told the *National Observer* that he felt the bond issue might not have succeeded if the grass were not real. "We understand air-conditioning and engineering down here, but not artificial grass. Now the stadium is up and the people are used to it. They'll accept artificial grass now, and I'll bet every major-league stadium has it in five years."[71]

Nearly fifty years later, Hofheinz aide Tal Smith was emphatic on this point: "If Hofheinz or the architects or anybody else had gone and said...'we're not only going to have a roof and air conditioning, but we're not going to be able to play on grass'... *no way* that would have ever been accomplished...you *had* to grow grass."[72]

So, after a month or two, the architects ended their foray into the world of artificial turf, and were fully engaged in the task of optimizing the roof design and getting real grass to grow. "We now feel that it is entirely possible to grow natural grass indoors and overcome most of the serious problems which go along with it,"[73] Anderson said in a letter to a prospective carpet vendor.

So Anderson and his colleagues would need to become experts on sunlight and grass. Architects are, of course, not trained in agronomy—it is likely that none of the Associated Architects knew much more about grass than how often to mow their front lawns. They needed consultants who could advise them on grass and how much light it would take to grow it.

Normally, architects hire structural, mechanical, and electrical engineers as consultants to provide specialized services for which architects are not trained. However, the light-and-grass issue was completely uncharted territory that called for different talents. The architects assembled a group of scientists, a team that eventually grew to eight physicists and agronomists.

One of the earliest hires was a physicist, Dr. Gerald C. Phillips, chairman of the Department of Physics at Rice. Phillips was brought on to advise on the quantity of light entering the building through skylights. Clearly relishing his task, Phillips treated the domed stadium as he would an academic research project. He hosted meetings in a classroom at Rice, where the architects and engineers gathered around while Phillips filled chalkboards with figures. He wrote lengthy papers, steeped in theory, meticulously footnoted and thick with formulas.

*The perfect dome would be one that transmitted all the light falling on it and focussed it in a diffused, uniform fashion upon the grass area* *alone. The minimum opening of such a perfect, and unattainable, dome would have an area $A_p$, related to the area of grass $A_g$, the incident light intensity $I_o$, and the necessary light intensity $I_g$ by*

$$A_p = (A_g I_g) / I_o$$

*If the playing field is 258' in radius, of area 209,000 ft.$^2$, $I_g$ = 1500 f.c. is chosen, and $I_o$ in mid-winter is taken at 2520 f.c. Then*

$$A_p > 125,000 \, ft.^2 \,\,^{74}$$

In the early days, Phillips was not optimistic about reconciling the need for sunlight against solar gain. On more than one occasion, he suggested changing the design to leave the roof off of the playing field and enclose the spectators only, as is done at some racetracks. But he soon threw himself into the problem of the big roof, crunching more numbers, and offering increasingly ambitious suggestions. The architects had ruled out a retractable roof due to concerns about the reliability of such a system.[75] Phillips proposed various dynamic systems mounted within the roof that would regulate daylight on the field. At meetings with the architects, he shared his concept sketches of a giant circular rotating shade, operable louvers, and inflatable Mylar bladders. Perhaps the most ambitious concept would have made the entire roof an inflatable, floating Mylar balloon tethered to the stadium walls by cables.[76]

In retrospect, it's tempting to smile at this succession of Rube Goldberg schemes, but Phillips was raising a crucial point: variable lighting would allow grass to grow while maintaining cooler temperatures for game time.

The AA would also need expert advice about the grass itself, so they hired agronomists as consultants. Like Phillips the physicist, most of the agronomists came from academic settings (the principal agronomist was Texas A&M professor William O. Trogdon) as well as from the U.S. Department of Agriculture's research facility at Greenbelt, Maryland. Private industry also got into the act: an agronomist from Toro Manufacturing consulted on the project.

From the outset, the agronomists were not very encouraging: their consensus was that the light available to grow grass in the stadium was at best marginal. Trogdon was able to suggest several varieties of grass that were known to do well in shade, but he noted that few of these grasses would be ideal for athletic-field applications. A playing field must, of course, withstand a high level of foot traffic. He pointed out that even with ample sunlight, it was difficult to maintain a good turf surface on football fields late in the season. Low light and marginal turf would exacerbate that problem. Early in 1962, Agronomist R.C Potts told Ralph Anderson that "a grass grown in reduced light has thin leaves, weak stems, long internodes [and] a weak poorly developed root system and thus would be easily damaged from play."[77] Presciently, Trogdon twice suggested that artificial turf would be a better choice, although he acknowledged that there was no such product on the market at the time.[78]

So in the face of mounting evidence of trouble down the road, the architects continued to pursue natural grass.

Since the agronomists were unanimously pessimistic about the perils of low light, the next logical question was *just how much light would be too little light?* Here the scientists' consensus started to fray and it seemed that no one was able to quantify the problem. It soon became apparent that Trogdon and his colleagues did not know just how much light was needed to grow grass—in fact, no one knew. Since grass grew almost exclusively outdoors, it simply had not been necessary to know.

At the same time, the roof design had to move forward, and the architects were forced to proceed using assumptions about the type and quantity of skylights that would be needed. Ralph Anderson fretted, "The success of this project rests on such a collection of assumptions and educated guesses."[79]

Since there was really no empirical data about grass performance under low light, the architects were compelled to produce their own data. They convinced the county to fund a study at Texas A&M's College of Agriculture to evaluate the performance of a variety of grasses under varying light levels. They designed a customized greenhouse for the experiment, ten feet wide by thirty feet long, but only three feet high. The roof comprised several samples of plastic skylight material, and it could be slid aside to allow the contents to be examined and clipped. Mounted on a side wall were two air conditioning

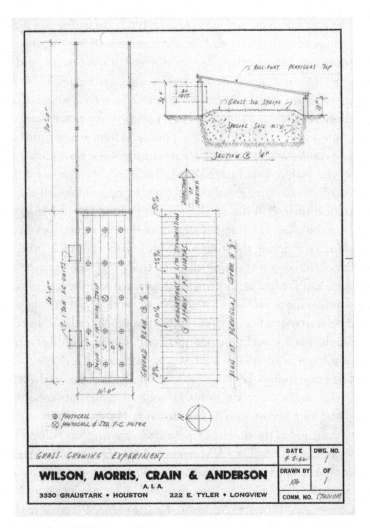

Architect's drawing showing the small greenhouse structure built at Texas A&M to evaluate grass growth indoors. *(Robert J. Minchew Houston Astrodome Architectural and Engineering Collection, 1928-1990, Dolph Briscoe Center for American History, The University of Texas at Austin)*

units intended to simulate the climate in the Dome. At the base of this elaborate little structure sat the laboratory test subjects—five strips of turf set in a special soil mix.

The first round of tests took place in 1962, evaluating five different species of grasses that had been recommended by Trogdon and his colleagues.* Two of these species emerged as the best adapted for growing in limited light—Bermudagrass and Zoysia grass. These two grasses were tested again the following year. This second round of tests served more or less as a runoff and as an opportunity to test more distinct light levels, as well as various clipping and fertilization regimes.

The results were on the surface promising—the grass grew—but below the surface problems loomed. Texas A&M professor Ethan Holt had visually monitored the progress of the samples all season, but only at the end of the experiment did he have an opportunity to examine the roots. His findings were troubling. "The maintenance of a surface cover during the study looked reasonably favorable until the quality of the cover was examined." The study concluded that "[e]ven though a satisfactory green surface was maintained, the lack of rooting depth and general lack of strength and depth of the turf suggests rapid deterioration under traffic, especially football traffic."[80] In other words, the grass would grow indoors and look good, until someone began using it as an athletic field.

The grass studies, begun in early 1961, lingered into early 1964. The other major technical hurdles—roof, acoustics, air conditioning—had long been resolved. Construction had been underway for over a year, and at the site the Dome's steel structure was rising.†

With the discouraging A&M report in hand, Anderson held a series of meetings with the Judge. Anderson reported that the grass would indeed grow, but it would be "very marginal." The meetings must have been tense ones. Here was Anderson, having presided over more than two years of research, with the Dome's steel superstructure topped out, telling his client that his baseball team might not have a viable grass surface on which to play. Talk about "dynamic" sun-control systems was briefly revived, but it was agreed that the cost would be prohibitive. Soon after, the architects, likely with an increasing sense of dread,

---

* Some accounts state that the grass was bred at Texas A&M specifically for use in the Astrodome, but this was not the case. The A&M Study evaluated and compared grasses that were already available. The grass that was ultimately selected for the Astrodome was Tifway 419, developed in 1960 at the U.S. Department of Agriculture's Tifton Experiment Station in Georgia.
† See Chapter 13.

began another round of inquiries with manufacturers in search of an artificial playing surface. But this search did not bring promising results, and Hofheinz decided that he had to accept the risk and move on.[81]

The Judge may even have quietly welcomed the news. In fact, Hofheinz had been talking about artificial grass for years, probably thinking of his need to rent the Dome for conventions and trade shows. Sunlight aside, there were lots of good reasons not to plant real grass in the new Domed Stadium. An artificial surface would greatly simplify the process of converting the stadium from baseball to football. For a convention or trade show, real grass would need to be cut into squares, removed from the field, and stored in a location where it could be kept damp.[82] It would be a constant headache for the building's operator.

Hofheinz had mentioned synthetic grass in the press as early as 1963, referring to it as "undertaker's grass" after the plastic covering used by funeral directors to discreetly conceal soil piled at gravesites. Perhaps as a result of Ralph Anderson's ominous grass reports in 1964, Hofheinz stepped up his public statements about artificial turf, taking every opportunity to point out that he intended to do away with the natural grass as soon as possible.

The natural grass would indeed be replaced, but much sooner than anyone expected.

CHAPTER **NINE**

# FALLOUT

ON THE EVENING OF JULY 25, 1961, President Kennedy soberly faced a television camera in the Oval Office and spoke to a nationwide audience about the threat posed by the Soviets, who were pressuring the Allies to leave West Berlin and preparing to seal off the city. This would become one of the most dangerous episodes in the Cold War, and Kennedy was compelled to make preparations for war with the Soviets over Germany. In the speech, he announced a $3.5 billion ($26.9 billion) package to boost America's military readiness: he wanted to increase manpower by over 217,000 troops by stepping up the draft and calling up reservists. Finally, he said that he would ask Congress for $207 million ($1.6 billion) for civil defense, and he told viewers at home about the importance of individual preparedness, dwelling on increased capacity for fallout shelters.

In his speech, and in the days following it, Kennedy hoped to raise public awareness of civil defense needs, and the dangers of a prolonged Cold War. Previous civil defense efforts had been mired in budget cuts and apathy. Most of those efforts had been devoted to communications infrastructure, and public education along the lines of "duck and cover." Construction of shelter facilities had been largely left to individuals and local authorities. Now, with a greatly increased risk of a "hot" war, the new president wanted fallout shelters—quickly. In his speech, the president said he would seek funds "to identify and mark space in existing structures—public and private—that could be used for fall-out shelters in case of attack."

Judge Hofheinz quickly made it known he had just such a structure in mind, although his building was not quite "existing." Kennedy's proposed civil defense funding included $13.5 million ($105.2 million) for shelter "research and development,"[83] and Hofheinz jumped at the chance to leverage federal money to help build the Dome. The stadium plans were quickly modified to show two new levels of basement space below the stands totaling 100,000 square feet.[84] Another series of revised plans were even more ambitious, showing one of the basement levels extended 300 feet beyond the building and below the parking lot, completely ringing the Dome like a doughnut. The resulting shelter space would be over twenty acres, which— according to Pentagon criteria—could accommodate 150,000 refugees.

The plan was that after a catastrophic nuclear attack, survivors would come to the Dome and take shelter for several weeks in the huge circular basement and below the stands (the seating areas and the playing field itself would be off limits because the skylights would have admitted radiation). A series of sprinklers would continually wash fallout off the domed roof. Drinking water would come from a new deep well. The revised plans, although hastily developed, depicted a facility that could save thousands of lives in a catastrophe.

Hofheinz and the county commissioners clearly saw an added benefit that was certainly no afterthought: this vast additional space, constructed with federal funds, would be available for exhibit space and parking on days when there was no catastrophe.

As mayor just eight years earlier, Hofheinz had been a shelter skeptic. In 1953, he had told the *Houston Press* that the only way to save lives in the event of nuclear attack would be to "completely evacuate the city."[85] Now, in 1961, his view had changed, and he waged a full-court press. He set off for an extended visit to Washington, where over the course of five days he met at least three times with Vice President Johnson and other administration officials, presumably to lobby for federal funding.[86] He brought along copies of an illustrated brochure describing the shelter proposal, complete with architect's drawings and cost data for the revised design. In what may have served as full disclosure, the brochure included a drawing showing a peacetime view of Brahman cattle on display in the shelter.[87] His friend (and

SHELTER   SHOWN  AS   FAT  STOCK  SHOW  EXHIBIT  AREA

During the 1961 Berlin Crisis, Judge Hofheinz traveled to Washington to seek federal funding for a massive fallout shelter beneath the Dome and parking areas. The shelter, constructed with Defense Department funding, would have been available for use as exhibit space, as shown in the sketch. *(RGD0005, Houston Public Library, HMRC)*

later biographer) Edgar Ray wrote a melodramatic what-if piece in the *Houston Press*, imagining his experiences during a two-week, post-attack stay in the Dome. (In one memorable scene, Ray is relieved to find that he and his fellow refugees will be allowed to smoke in the shelter—thanks to the Dome's smoker-friendly ventilation system—but frets that he has brought only one pack to last two weeks.)[88]

President Kennedy was always mindful of Texas in his reelection plans. Traditionally Democratic, it was emerging as a swing state for the 1964 election. His administration, at least at the outset, seemed eager to help. By the end of August, the Defense Department proposed a federal grant of $750,000 ($6 million) to Harris County—believed to be the largest single such grant in the government's research-and-development program for fallout shelters.[89] This was a promising start, but the shelter plans being drawn up by the architects would require significantly more money to construct. Estimates of the additional cost for these designs varied between $2 million and $8 million ($16 million and $63 million). The architects and engineers traveled to Washington for a meeting with Pentagon officials, who helpfully provided suggestions on items that would be eligible for federal funding.

Hofheinz was pursuing the shelter idea not just to leverage additional exhibit space, but also out of increasing concern that the building could not be delivered on the county budget alone.[90] Simply put, he needed the federal cash, judiciously allocated in order to finish the project. Of course, that government funding was intended to be limited to costs directly due to the addition of the shelter facilities. But such allocations are not always cut-and-dried, and the related cost analysis is frequently and inherently subjective. With Kennedy seeking favor in the Lone Star State, and with a Texan vice president and powerful congressional leadership, it is likely that Hofheinz and his designers were expecting a favorable outcome in Washington. As a result, the fallout shelter remained in the plans, even though the funding deal was not yet in place. It would prove to be a costly distraction.

PART THREE

# BUILDING A DOME

CHAPTER **TEN**

# BREAKING GROUND

January 3, 1962: Dignitaries fire pistols to break ground for the new Domed Stadium. Photo by Darling Photography. *(George Kirksey Papers, Courtesy of Special Collections, University of Houston Libraries)*

ON A COLD JANUARY MORNING IN 1962, politicians, oilmen, engineers, and reporters converged on a site off South Main Street, five miles from downtown Houston. The site where they gathered was a 250-acre patch of Gulf Coastal Prairie, which at the time was almost entirely vacant. Among the few man-made structures visible on the site were a few pumping oil wells, marking the northern fringe of the great Pierce Junction oil field. Forty years earlier, Pierce Junction, just a mile to the south, had been the first big strike in the Houston area, and it remained one of the earliest landmarks of the city's prosperity.

Now a new landmark would rise on this site. Nearby, the Texas flag flew on a tall pole on the future site of home plate. Below it fluttered the team flag of Houston's new major league baseball team, the Colt .45s.

The group proceeded to a small stage that had been set up for the occasion. There they lined up, and each man was issued a weapon. It was time to break ground for the world's first air-conditioned, domed stadium.

As is normal in a large-scale project, selecting that site had presented a considerable political challenge. Three years earlier, just after being awarded the commission, one of the Associated Architects' initial tasks had been to conduct a site-selection study for what at the time was still envisioned as a traditional open stadium. As an initial step, they identified a number of potential sites of adequate size (at least 200 acres would be needed) around the city.

The search was conducted almost entirely among suburban sites. Amid Houston's growth and prosperity at mid century, the city had started to sprawl, the process of gradual unwinding that became a characteristic of every large American city during the period. Downtown high rises built on the antebellum original plat remained, but they were now competing for tenants with smaller, two- or three-story office buildings that were springing up on major roads leading out of the city, toward emerging suburbs to the west and south.

Notably, only one downtown site had even been considered for the new stadium, and only at the urging of the mayor of Houston.[91] It was quickly dropped from consideration, and the remaining sites were all at least five miles outside downtown. These were evaluated using uniform criteria that largely reflected the suburban ethos of the city and of the time. Parking and auto accessibility were high on the list of priorities: without them, as Kirksey had told the architects, "all would be lost before we ever threw a ball or swung a bat."[92] The state Highway Department provided this evaluation on the basis of existing and planned roadways. Other criteria considered what lay at the other end of those roads—nearby hotels and restaurants, and the demographics of the areas within a twenty-five-minute driving radius, projected to the year 1980.[93] Availability of public transit was not a factor, because Houston in 1958 had virtually no public transit system.* The planning criteria, in other words, were more or less what would be used to select a suburban shopping center site.

As for any large project, availability of land was a major factor; multiple owners and residential uses are disadvantages in assembling land for development, whether public or private. Harris County had the power to take property by eminent domain, but like many public agencies they were reluctant to use it, particularly for a sports-and-entertainment facility.

The analysis pointed toward three locations, the most favorable of which was a portion of Memorial Park, about five miles northwest of downtown Houston. The 1,466-acre park could readily accommodate a 200-acre stadium facility and was well positioned in the roadway network, adjacent to Houston's affluent and rapidly growing west side. Here, however, the logical and objective site-selection process ran up against the most important criterion of all—politics, and political influence.

Land for Memorial Park had been sold to the city of Houston in 1925 by descendants of former Texas Governor James Stephen Hogg. The Hogg family had amassed tremendous wealth in oil. The sale was conditioned on the use of the property as parkland, and the Hogg family retained the right to refuse any other use. Hogg's daughter Ima,[†] an influential philanthropist still living in Houston, now invoked that right, threatening to take back the entire park. The county and Parks Board quickly backed down. Talbott Wilson later wrote, "In the end, it was impossible to find anyone who would admit to

---

* Houston dismantled its streetcar system in 1940, as did many other American cities around that time. In the late 1950s, a private company operated bus service under a city concession. Those buses primarily carried domestic help from their homes on the East Side to their jobs in River Oaks and other affluent areas. Former Houston Mayor Fred Hofheinz, Interview by Frank Michel, February 11, 2008. Houston Public Library, Houston Oral History Project

† That was indeed her real name. According to the *Handbook of Texas*, "Ima was named for the heroine of a Civil War poem written by her uncle Thomas Elisha. Her name became a part of Texas folklore, along with the myth of a fictitious sister supposedly named Ura." Virginia Bernhard, "HOGG, IMA," *Handbook of Texas Online* (http://www.tshaonline.org/handbook/online/articles/fho16), accessed June 19, 2013. Published by the Texas State Historical Association

having made the suggestion."[94] Thus, Memorial Park was spared, and it remains one of Houston's most treasured assets.

Two sites remained on the short list, but, leery of further controversy, the Parks Board had suspended the site search until a baseball franchise was in hand.

By 1960, as HSA's efforts moved closer to fruition, attention returned to site selection, specifically to the South Main site, which had much to recommend it. Half a million people lived within a 25-minute drive, and projections showed that by 1980, they would gain over 800,000 new neighbors. The site was highly rated by both Houston City Planning and the Texas Highway Department, primarily because freeway access was superb—the proposed route of a South Loop Freeway passed directly through the site, and a new South Freeway was being realigned to pass about a mile to the east, creating a major highway interchange virtually adjacent to the site.

The site was attractive to the county and the designers because it was almost entirely vacant and comprised just a few large tracts of land under single ownership. The land was, for the most part, in friendly hands, held by large institutions such as Hermann Hospital, Houston Fat Stock, Hilton Hotels—and R.E. "Bob" Smith.*

The site was procured in August 1961, when Smith and Hofheinz purchased the 494-acre Hilton tract, combined it with Smith's land, and then sold the stadium site back to the county at cost. Shrewdly, they saved for themselves several choice parcels surrounding the site, property that could be privately developed to capture some of the value of the huge facility next door.

Now, for the 1962 groundbreaking ceremony, a reporter had suggested that ground be broken not with the traditional gold shovels but instead with Colt .45s, the new team's namesake. The single-action revolvers were real, but thanks to someone's good sense, loaded with wax blank cartridges.

---

* Land at the other short-listed site east of downtown was also owned by Smith. While this might make some suspect an insider deal, it is more likely that Smith's vast land holdings around Houston would have overlapped just about any large site acquisition in the city. "Preliminary Architectural Program and Site Area Considerations for A Sport Center for Harris County" ca. 1958. Minchew Box 94-274-1.

Groups of men took turns lining up in front of the dais, and posed for photographers, firing into the tall grass. The county commissioners came first, followed by the HSA leadership.

At one point, the dignitaries stepped back to make room for another group—Quentin Mease, joined by two other African-American businessmen who were well-known and respected in their community. They had been invited to participate by Judge Hofheinz,[95] and their presence symbolized a tacit agreement that the new stadium would be integrated. Like the other groups, these men smiled for the cameras while holding their weapons, but due to the local press blackout, their photos did not appear in the next day's newspapers.*

The Colt .45s fired one last time. Amid the applause, forty-five aerial shells were set off above home plate.

It was time to build.

---

*A copy of the photo was preserved by Quentin R. Mease, and appears in Thomas R. Cole's *No Color Is My Kind: The Life of Eldrewey Stearns and the Integration of Houston.*

CHAPTER **ELEVEN**

# A BIG HOLE IN THE GROUND

BUILDING, IN THIS CASE, began with digging a hole. Constructing any new building normally begins with excavation for foundations and utilities, but the Dome was a special case. Its six-tier seating areas would rise the equivalent of ten stories above the playing field, which was set 25 feet below grade. This was done for the convenience of persons entering the building; roughly half would walk down to their seats, and the others would have a relatively short climb up. This was more convenient for spectators, and reduced reliance on large ramps and expensive escalators. Lloyd and Morgan had successfully applied this concept eleven years earlier at Rice Stadium.

Therefore, the initial excavation would be exceptionally large— over 700 feet in diameter and 24 feet deep. Digging it would take time—months, actually—during which little if any other construction could take place. Meanwhile, the building plans were incomplete and the Dome's design team was still working to an aggressive schedule, with opening planned for 1963. The team agreed to take a schedule shortcut, letting a separate contract for excavation while at the same time continuing to work on the final plans. Architects and contractors refer to this as *fast-tracking*, and it has long been a common practice for projects under tight schedules.[*]

The excavation contract was awarded to John S. Kraak Company in December 1961. The groundbreaking ceremony, held the following month, marked the start of that company's work digging the great

---

[*] One of the better-known examples of a fast-tracked building is the Pentagon, which had been constructed just 20 years earlier in Arlington, Virginia.

This 1963 photo gives an idea of the scale of the excavation needed to construct the Domed Stadium. The excavation was over 700 feet in diameter and 24 feet deep. Colt Stadium is seen in the background. (*RGD0005, Houston Public Library, HMRC*)

hole. Kraak got to work immediately, and finished the job on schedule the following May.

The great hole was the first physical evidence of the scale of the structure that was to follow, and it was an impressive sight. Visitors would approach it by climbing a slight rise of earth around the perimeter. When they reached the top, the huge circular excavation was dramatically revealed. It reminded some of the Grand Canyon, although it was, of course, nowhere near that large. It just seemed that way.

By April 1962, another impressive sight had appeared: in just a matter of months, a new temporary outdoor ballpark had sprouted adjacent to the growing excavation. The Colt .45s would make their major league debut in the 1962 season, and would need a place to play while the Domed Stadium was under construction. The problem was not an unusual one: frequently, when a sports franchise is established in or moved to a new city, the team plays in an existing stadium until a new park is constructed.

For Houston, the conventional, fiscally prudent solution would have been to have the new team play in old Buff Stadium, but Hofheinz would have none of it. The minor-league park had just 14,000 seats and lacked parking. Moreover, the Grand Huckster saw an opportunity to generate excitement for the new Domed Stadium by locating the temporary venue next to the construction site, so that spectators would see for themselves the innovative new structure rising alongside. A scaffolding company was hired to construct the new 32,000-seat Colt Stadium at a cost of $2 million ($15.4 million). The galvanized steel and wood structure was erected in about four months, another milestone in Houston's history of short-order buildings such as Sam Houston Hall and Rice Stadium. As at Rice, Colt Stadium's construction went down to the wire, with the parking lot still being paved early in the morning of opening day. It was there that the Houston Colt .45s hosted Houston's first major league baseball game, on April 10, 1962.*

Meanwhile, as the Colt .45s performed in their new temporary ballpark, and Kraak's bulldozers and excavators clawed into the site, design work continued in the architects' offices. Though construction was under way, the drawings for the building itself were only about 76 percent complete. Under a fast-track schedule, this was normal. Most of the major technology questions had been settled the previous year (the grass being a notable exception), and the architects were able to make progress in turning the idea of the Dome into reality.

As the plans advanced in early 1962, there was increasing concern about the $15 million budget for the building itself. After nearly a year of active discussion about the fallout shelter, it was clear that the design team had come to expect that the Defense Department would make a substantial contribution to the cost of the new stadium.

Current events, however, were moving in a different direction. By spring 1962, the Berlin crisis had concluded, thankfully not with a

---

* The team would play three seasons in Colt Stadium and, by all accounts, conditions there underscored the need for an indoor venue. Ballplayers and spectators wilted under the high heat and humidity, and were feasted on by mosquitos drawn to the damp, low-lying site. When the Astrodome opened in 1965, the outdoor stadium was abandoned, and sat moldering on the site for years. In the late 1960s, it was disassembled and the components purchased by a Mexican businessman, who trucked the pieces to Torreon, Mexico. There, the ballpark was reassembled and became known as *El Mecano*—The Erector Set.

Colt Stadium with the excavation for the Domed Stadium in background. Erected in about four months, it was the temporary home of the Colt .45s for three seasons. Colt Stadium was abandoned after the Astrodome opened in 1965, and later disassembled and shipped to Torreon, Mexico, where it became the home of a Mexican League team in the 1970s. *(RGD0005, Houston Public Library, HMRC)*

bang but with construction of a wall sealing off West Berlin, which Kennedy reluctantly accepted, concluding that the wall was "a hell of a lot better than a war."[96] Amid reduced international tension, the government's interest in fallout shelters was waning, and potential funding for the Dome shelter was dwindling.

In May, word arrived that the federal participation would be limited to $750,000 (the amount originally promised the previous year), and that would be offered on a matching basis. Moreover, the federal funds were expected to come with strings attached in the form of stricter construction criteria for the stadium. It was an easy deal to turn down, and the Commissioner's Court did so promptly. At a meeting held on May 22, 1962, the architects were instructed to prepare a plan to complete the building without the shelter and within the original $15 million budget. They agreed to return in a week to present that plan.

However, it was becoming clear that the building could not be delivered at that price. As is frequently the case with large and complex projects, cost estimates steadily mounted as the unprecedented building's many unknowns were recognized and addressed. Even the cancelled fallout shelter was continuing to influence costs. Once planning for the shelter had begun, provisions for it had been incorporated in the design, and had remained for months amid the uncertainty over federal funding. The huge circular basement beneath the parking lots surrounding the Dome had long since been dropped from the plans, but the shelter directly below the stands remained in the design.[97] In fact, that space had already been excavated by Kraak, and now it would require additional concrete perimeter walls, floors, power and ventilation. It was a classic case of the perils of fast-track construction, and what design and construction industry professionals call *scope creep*—the tendency of projects to grow due to many small ad hoc changes. Now, with a hole dug large enough for a fallout shelter but no money to pay for the shelter, it was time to face facts on the construction budget.

The unpleasant task of breaking this news to the county commissioners fell to the architects' spokesman, Si Morris. Morris, by this time, had been with the project for nearly four years, and his frontman duties were taking a toll. He had stopped playing golf because other golfers were pestering him with questions about the high-profile project. His son had asked him, "Dad, how far will we have to move when the Dome falls down?"[98]

On May 28, in what must have been a nerve-wracking presentation, Morris informed the commissioners that the $15 million budget would not be sufficient to complete the building. As if that news was not bad enough, Morris then went on to tell his clients that he did not know exactly how much the project in its current form would cost. "If this were a standardized type of structure, whether a residence or a multistory office building, we could project a reasonably exact estimate," he explained. However, the Dome was hardly a standardized type of structure. "In this instance, you and we have set out to build a structure for which there is no prototype,"[99] Morris told the commissioners.

Asked how the project had arrived at this juncture, Morris offered some interesting explanations. He stated that the early estimates for the building itself were based on estimates for proposed similar stadiums in New York City, Los Angeles, and Washington, D.C., all of which estimates had later proved to be low.[*] He also explained that the architects had been relying on other funding sources, including the fallout shelter grant, seat-option income, and savings from civil works—in other words, they had always expected to have more money available beyond the $15 million budget. Finally, he cited the additional costs resulting from shelter space below the stands, which would be retained in the new design solely as convention and exhibit space.

Most remarkable of all was Morris's suggested plan for moving the project forward. Rather than having the architects and engineers attempt to estimate the cost, he recommended that the construction documents (then 76 percent complete) be finished and sent out for bids by contractors. Normally, owners expect to know the approximate cost of a building before they seek bids from contractors, and usually architects or cost estimators are paid to provide that advance information. Now the bids themselves would provide the cost data needed for leadership to make an informed decision. In other words, the marketplace would provide the cost data traditionally provided by the architects and engineers. It was, to say the least, an audacious plan, and one that Morris could not have proposed without the agreement of Hofheinz (who was uncharacteristically silent in the press accounts of this period).

Predictably, the commissioners were less than thrilled with Morris's presentation and its implications. They had authorized and paid for a giant hole in the ground and now had no assurance that they could afford the building intended to fill it. Adding insult to injury, the county had to pay $3,200 ($24,700) per week to pump groundwater out of the hole.[†]

---

[*] Respectively Shea Stadium, Dodgers Stadium, and Washington (now RFK) Stadium, all of which were being designed or in construction at the time the Astrodome was designed, and all of which indeed experienced cost overruns.

[†] Pumping, or dewatering, is frequently necessary on construction projects to remove groundwater, which naturally collects in a deep excavation. In this case the problem was exacerbated because the hole would be left open for many months while the construction documents were completed. Carol Foley, "$3200 a Week For Dry Hole," *Houston Chronicle* 7/11/1962

Judge Elliott and the other commissioners took many hits in the press, and in letters from constituents. A newspaper columnist suggested that the pumps be shut off so that the resulting body of water could be used for recreational purposes and called Lake Elliott (named, of course, for the sitting county judge) or that the county court's offices be moved to the bottom of the pit from which they could continue to operate the county in a hole to match the fiscal one they had managed themselves into.[100]

Of course, in the world of public construction, some might have viewed the situation as a blessing. If estimated costs rise too high during the planning stage, a project can be readily cancelled at relatively low political and financial cost. However, with millions of construction dollars sunk—many of them literally—in the Domed Stadium, terminating the project would have been nearly impossible from a political standpoint. Robert Moses, New York's autocratic public works czar, was fond of saying, "Once you sink that first stake, they'll never make you pull it up."

Indeed, the county commissioners did not seem to consider terminating the high-profile project. To their credit, they did not take the easy out by eliminating the domed roof. (Perhaps anticipating this question, Morris had told them that the remaining funds would be sufficient to build "no more than a first-class domeless and therefore un-airconditioned stadium,"[101] a statement that managed to combine a boast and a threat.) The consensus among the commissioners was that the dome was a necessity. Having ruled out killing the project and slashing the design, they were left with no choice but to go with Morris's plan—finish the drawings, put the project out to bid, and hope for the best.

Over the summer of 1962, the architects and engineers worked to complete the plans and specifications, and they were put out for bids that October. There were a total of 357 sheets in the bid drawing set,[102] a rather low figure for such a large structure and an indicator of the Dome's architectural simplicity. The bids were due in November.

Now it would be up to the marketplace, and the politicians and architects could only await the results.

CHAPTER **TWELVE**

# COST PLUS A DOLLAR

THE COUNTY COMMISSIONERS HAD FEARED that contractors would not be willing to spend the money to make bids on a project with such an iffy outlook. But Morris had predicted that they would, and they did. In the fall of 1962, five firms were working feverishly to come to grips with all of the unknowns and preparing to submit bids on the world's first air-conditioned domed stadium.

The November night before bids were due, Al Jensen, an executive of contractor H.A. Lott, had put in a late night preparing his company's bid. Lott had joined forces with Minneapolis-based contractors Johnson, Drake, and Piper to bid on the project, and their joint venture became known as "Lott-Drake." Jensen and his colleagues had misgivings about their task—the word on the street was that George Brown, who had famously built Rice Stadium at cost twelve years earlier, was planning to bid on the Dome "at cost plus a dollar."[103] It so happened that while a student at Rice, Jensen had had a summer job with Brown & Root on the Rice Stadium project. He had been a carpenter's helper on the column crew, working eleven-hour days, seven days a week, stacking forms from the Gulf Freeway overpasses. Brown, of course, was a regular in Suite 8-F, a very formidable competitor, and clearly local pride was a factor. Some were saying that since Brown & Root was going to bid at cost, any other firm that prepared a bid was wasting its time.

When the estimators finished their work, Lott-Drake's bid stood at $19,440,000 ($150,030,000). The forms were signed, and the next morning Jensen went over to the Commissioners Court to submit it.

The bids, as is customary for a public project, would be opened in public, and the room was rapidly filling with reporters and contractors eager to learn the results. As the crowd pressed in, Jensen was nudged toward the front of the room and found himself standing directly behind County Judge Bill Elliott, the man who would open and read the sealed bids stacked next to his seat.

The first envelope Elliott opened was from Brown & Root. Standing behind the Judge, Jensen was close enough to read the total: $24,792,000—a bid more than $5 million *higher* than Lott-Drake's.

Jensen was horrified. If Brown & Root had accurately estimated the job and were indeed bidding it at cost, Lott-Drake stood to lose millions. Jensen had to resist the impulse to reach over and snatch Lott-Drake's unopened bid from the stack and put it in his pocket.[104]

But as the other bids were opened, Jensen was able to relax a little. The three remaining firms had submitted much lower bids, between $19.7 million and $20.7 million ($152 million and $160 million). The estimators at Brown & Root had apparently not sharpened their pencils, and their firm was left as an outlier with by far the highest bid.

Lott-Drake, and Al Jensen, had won the job.

With the bids in hand, the county commissioners now knew the real cost of the project. They lost no time scheduling a $9.6 million ($74 million) bond referendum to make up the shortfall, and made preparations for a remarkable third trip to the public-funding well. Once again, Hofheinz targeted African-American votes, sending sound trucks throughout Houston's Third, Fourth, and Fifth ward neighborhoods. The sound trucks played recordings of Willie Mays, Hank Aaron, and Ernie Banks imploring baseball fans to vote for the bond issue, and to turn on their porch lights if they needed a ride to the polls. The voices of African-American ballplayers boomed over the loudspeakers into the streets: "If you all want to see me play here, you all vote for that dome."[105] The election was held on December 22, 1962—the Saturday before Christmas—so turnout was light, but the margin of victory was even higher than the 1961 referendum. Construction of the building itself could finally proceed.

# CHAPTER THIRTEEN

# THE DOME TAKES SHAPE

THE GREAT PIT had been sitting empty for twenty-two months when Lott-Drake finally started pouring foundations on March 27, 1963. A small ceremony was held at the site to mark the occasion, but this time no shots were fired. Members of the Houston consular corps placed small trinkets from their home countries into a capsule embedded in the concrete.[106] Finally, the building itself was under way. Over the following weeks, new foundation walls slowly encircled the perimeter of the pit, creating a circle 710 feet in diameter. As the concrete foundations cured, construction of the steel superstructure began, and the building started to take shape.

Structural engineers refer to domes as *shell structures*—meaning that, like an eggshell or oyster shell, the dome supports itself without the aid of interior columns. To build such a structure, it is usually necessary to use temporary supports, or *falsework*, to hold up the dome until it is able to support itself. For the Domed Stadium, this temporary support was provided by thirty-seven steel erection towers, spaced evenly in two concentric rows around a single 200-foot-high tower at the apex.[107] The open-framed steel towers bore an uncanny resemblance to the oil derricks that had once dotted the landscape nearby. Huge cranes with 270-foot booms lifted the structural members into place atop the erection towers, starting with the primary longitudinal girders, radiating from the center like spokes on a bicycle wheel. Like fireworks bursting in slow motion, the structure took shape.

September 1963: the great roof takes shape, supported by temporary erection towers.
*(Robert J. Minchew Houston Astrodome Architectural and Engineering Collection, 1928-
1990, Dolph Briscoe Center for American History, The University of Texas at Austin. Peter
Whitney photo, courtesy Mike McCorkle)*

A massive *tension ring* surrounded the entire roof structure. A tension ring acts like the metal hoops on a wooden barrel, gathering and resisting all of the outward forces created by the weight of the dome above. Without the tension ring, the dome structure would flatten and spread out horizontally. As the dome structure and tension ring were assembled atop the towers, the structure began to resemble a shallow upside-down bowl.

At the same time the inverted bowl was taking shape, a steel superstructure was rising below to meet it. The supporting walls had been designed by Walter P. Moore, a Houston-based structural engineering firm responsible for all structural design below the proprietary Lamella roof structure.[108] While the great domed roof grabbed most of the headlines, there were also comparable innovations below. Moore developed a steel superstructure with pinned connections that allowed the dome to expand and contract due to temperature and wind, along with an ingenious system of buried cables and concrete deadmen that allowed the relatively thin concrete foundation walls (which had been extended three stories down to accommodate the now-defunct fallout shelter) to resist lateral soil pressure.[109]

Around this time, Hofheinz started to come to grips with the scale of what he was building, most notably its height. The top seating deck of the new stadium would be 107 feet above the playing field, and set back horizontally over 160 feet. From that height and distance, it would be difficult to see the action on the field. The Judge might have first noticed this when the steel structure was taking shape in late 1963, or perhaps just while pondering one of several architect's models of the new stadium. He kept one of those models at his home, where it resided on the dining room table. He had placed it on a lazy susan in the center of the table, so that it could readily be viewed from multiple angles. One day, he beckoned his daughter Dene into the dining room to look at the model with him. Years later, Dene recalled their discussion with great clarity.

"See these seats here?" he asked as he slowly rotated the model and pointed at the seats around the top tier of the stadium. "Would *you* want to sit up in those seats?" Well, no, thought Dene. Looking at the model, she could tell that the seats would be far from the action on the field. The Judge gave his daughter a cocky grin.

"You watch, I'm gonna make them the most expensive seats in the house."[110]

The Judge ordered up last-minute changes to the plans. In the original design, the top deck would have just three rows of seats in front of an aisle, beyond which would be massive sheet-metal ducts that encircled the entire stadium at this level. The ducts would have measured up to 48 by 76 inches—large enough for nearly anyone to walk inside. Now, Hofheinz had other plans for the space those ducts occupied.

Midway through construction, and only a year before the Dome was to open, the Judge ordered the design changed to relocate those ducts to a lower level. Although the ductwork was not yet constructed, it was a disruptive and expensive change, requiring dozens of drawings to be revised and material to be reordered. Hofheinz would not let the complaints of his architects and contractors dissuade him.

"Roy Hofheinz wanted it done and it got built," Fred Hofheinz said years later.[111] The modified plans would indeed be built, and, as will be seen, become one of the Astrodome's lasting innovations.

Meanwhile, the steel structure continued to rise. The building was topped out in November, 1963 when the last piece of the roof structure was lifted into place and the Dome was finally able to support itself. When the time came to remove the falsework, the temporary towers were lowered. It was a tricky operation because the tower supports had to be lowered simultaneously with huge winches. On February 4, 1964, the last winch was turned and the great roof was standing on its own.[112] With the full weight of the dome bearing on the structure below the tension ring, the stadium settled 4 3/16 inches, which was about 1/16 of an inch less than the structural engineers had predicted using their slide rules.

With the steel roof finally in place, the temporary towers were dismantled, and by mid-March it was for the first time possible to stand inside and get a sense of the scale of what would become the biggest room in the world. It also presented a long-awaited opportunity to deal with one of the great unknowns of indoor baseball: would batted balls strike the roof?

It was one of many questions being posed as the Dome took shape. Much as fifteenth-century man wondered whether a ship sailing too far would fall off the end of a flat earth, there were doubts about the vast new indoor space and the science of indoor baseball. Would curve balls curve? Would a batted ball carry longer or shorter? What would it be like to play on a perfectly level surface, as opposed to the graded "crown" necessary to drain an outdoor field? Would it rain indoors? Would the sound of a batted ball be different indoors and therefore confuse fielders? Would the indoor stadium make it hard for the Astros to adjust to other parks?[113] Now, as the massive structure neared completion, it would become possible to answer some of those questions.

In September, the Philadelphia Phillies were in town. Their relief pitcher Ed Roebuck was considered one of the best *fungo* hitters in baseball at the time. A fungo is a practice fly ball hit to an outfielder, usually with a specially designed fungo bat. Roebuck and his fungo

This January, 1964 photo shows the completed dome as it was slowly lowered onto the vertical superstructure below. *(Harris County Archives, Peter Whitney photo courtesy Mike McCorkle.)*

bat were enlisted to step into the unfinished Dome to try to hit the roof. Standing at the future location of home plate, Roebuck took about two dozen swings. On each attempt he would toss a ball in the air, lean way back, and try to hit the ball straight up. He hit the roof structure at least once above the first base area, where the roof was approximately 190 feet above the field. This was not an alarming result: under game conditions, a hitter's objective is generally distance, not height, and fungo bats were not allowed in an actual game. Roebuck declared the roof safe from batted balls.[114]

A few months later, another test took place when legendary pitcher Satchel Paige was invited to toss a few pitches inside the building, which was now fully enclosed. As an African-American, Paige had been barred from major league baseball and relegated to the Negro Leagues while in his prime. Now at age fifty-eight, surrounded by photographers, he was still a formidable presence on the mound as he threw pitches, wearing a borrowed Astros uniform. Did his curve balls behave normally indoors? In Paige's words: "No difference under the Dome than anyplace else. My curve breaks good here, but I don't know about them young pitchers. Maybe they ain't got no curve to break." He went on to predict that deep fences and lack of fickle breezes would make the Dome "a pitcher's paradise,"[115] and as it turned out, he was absolutely correct.

During the time that the Domed Stadium had been on the architects' drafting boards, the space program and NASA were receiving a great deal of attention around the country, and in Houston. Thanks once again to a powerful Texas congressional delegation, NASA's Manned Spacecraft Center had been established in Houston in 1961, and the wildly famous Mercury Seven astronauts had arrived during the summer of 1962. By 1964, two thousand employees were moving into a new headquarters campus that had risen in Clear Lake, twenty-one miles southeast of Houston and the Domed Stadium.

In December 1964, Hofheinz announced that the Colt .45s would change their name to the Astros. The new name was, of course, a nod to the excitement and rising influence of the space program around the country and a reminder that that program was now based in Houston. The Judge had originally preferred "Astronauts" but believed that sportswriters would seek a shorter name, and Hofheinz, as always, wanted to control the message. The name Colt .45s may have played to popular perceptions of Texas, but it was never really suited to Houston, a port city that identified more with commerce and the Gulf Coast than with cowboys or wagon trains.

There was another, perhaps more important, reason for the switch: the name Colt .45 was still controlled by the Colt Firearms Company, a gun manufacturer that remained very much in business. The company had previously agreed to allow the baseball team to use both the name and the image of the revolver in its logo. However, Colt's management believed they should share in revenues from the team's merchandise bearing the name. Judge Hofheinz thought otherwise, and changed the name, replacing the six-shooter with shooting stars on the team's jerseys—and its merchandise.

Just a few days after the Astros name was introduced, Hofheinz and Bob Smith gathered the new stadium's principal tenants and held a press conference to announce another name change: henceforth, the new stadium would be called the Astrodome. The official name would remain Harris County Domed Stadium, an uninspiring mouthful that Hofheinz had derided as too long to fit on the scoreboard.

The county commissioners did not attend the ceremony and did not seem to welcome this development. This was most likely because the new name, however catchy, obscured the politicians' credit for the achievement. Hofheinz's successor, County Judge Elliott, said, "They can call it what they like but the official name is still Harris County Domed Stadium. I am confident the [new] name is not in keeping with the wishes of the people." Elliot lost this skirmish in the court of public opinion but stuck to his guns. The following year, his congratulatory message in the opening-day program *Inside the Astrodome* snubbed the nickname and made pointed references to the "Harris County Domed Stadium." For years, the local papers stuck with the official name as well.

As 1964 turned to 1965, it appeared that all of the puzzle pieces had finally fallen into place. The great domed roof was topped out, precast concrete grandstands were being installed, and two acres of sod were being pampered and cultivated in soil taken from the building site at a sod farm in Wharton, Texas. There would be no more delays. The Astrodome would open for the 1965 baseball season.

# CHAPTER FOURTEEN

# LIKE A MILLION SUNS

*"Within the limitations of $45 million, the Astrodome is as perfect as possible."*
— JUDGE HOFHEINZ[116]

PERHAPS THE MOST MEMORABLE PROCLAMATION on Sunday April 4, 1965, came not from a pulpit but in the pages of the *Houston Chronicle*'s *Texas Sunday* magazine: "An era ends Friday. Houstonians may stop suffering while being entertained. No longer will their faces burn red in the semi-tropical sun. No longer must they perspire for the pleasure of watching experts at play."

The following Wednesday, the newly minted Astros left their spring training camp in Cocoa, Florida, and flew to Houston. With five days remaining before the start of the regular season, it was early to break camp, but the Astros needed time to get used to their brand-new ballpark and gain at least a little "home field advantage."

For many players that day, this was their first-ever look inside the Dome. The massive structure was now complete, and it was an impressive sight. Eighteen-year-old rookie Larry Dierker was amazed at what he saw and years later recalled the moment exactly. "I felt," he said, "like I had walked into the next century."[117] Dierker and his teammates wandered around inside the huge structure, jokingly hailing each other

The Astrodome in 1965. (*George Kirksey Papers, Courtesy of Special Collections, University of Houston Libraries*)

along the length of the ridiculously long dugouts,* and stopping to gawk whenever the giant electronic scoreboard was tested.

The grass had also arrived. Nurtured and pampered in soil from the Dome site at a turf farm in Wharton, Texas, it had been rolled up, trucked in, and placed in the building the previous winter. It was proving challenging to maintain—the groundskeepers were finding that with little sun and no wind to dry it out, it couldn't be watered too much. But it looked fine. The skylights and the diffusers worked exactly as planned: bright sunlight was evenly distributed on the field, and no shadows were visible.

Taking the field for the first time for a practice session, the players satisfied themselves that thrown and batted balls behaved more or less the same inside the Dome as outside. The hitters' background view from the batter's box was good, and given the truly level playing field,

---

* At both Colt Stadium and the Astrodome, Hofheinz had mandated 120-foot long dugouts to increase the number of seats "behind the dugout."

the fielders had a good view of the batter. (To improve drainage, a typical outdoor field is "crowned" to create a slight downward slope from the center to the perimeter; for baseball the crown can limit visibility of the batter from the outfield.) The infield grass was neither too slow nor too fast. For the ballplayers doing their jobs, it looked like business as usual. Relief pitcher Hal Woodeshick was asked how his curve balls were breaking indoors. "I don't know," he shrugged, "I ain't got a curve ball."[118]

Several players, however, were having some trouble tracking fly balls. The 4,596 Lucite skylights had been designed to diffuse bright sunlight, and they did that job well—too well, as it turned out. Rather than limit the painful glare of direct sunshine to a single orb in the sky, the diffusing layer of the skylights spread it over a much larger area. Players stumbled around, assuming a defensive posture when a ball headed for the roof and then missing it completely when it fell to earth. Veteran coach Nellie Fox took his glove and went onto the field, presumably to show the youngsters a thing or two. Eyebrows were raised when even he misjudged several flies.

At first, general manager Paul Richards and field manager Luman Harris confidently dismissed the problem. Harris muttered that the players should have worn their sunglasses. Richardson, glancing at his watch, noticed it was 4:30 P.M. and surmised that the problem might be limited to late afternoons. They agreed that the arc lights might help and agreed to turn them on for the following day's practice.

The barrage of misjudged balls continued, however, all witnessed by reporters who were milling about, watching the "historic" first practice in the Dome. Richards became concerned and made his way to the outfield to have a look for himself. When he returned to the sidelines, he asked a group of sportswriters how many day games were on the Astros' 1965 schedule. When he heard the answer was twenty-one, Richardson frowned.

"I didn't realize it was that many."[119]

As darkness fell outside and an intrasquad scrimmage began, the roof turned dark and the problem disappeared. There was no problem tracking the ball against the dark roof under the arc lights. Everyone relaxed a bit. The highlight of the evening came when Astros second

The caption on this April 9, 1965 photo read, "Houston players and managers seek solution to tricky problem." Left to right: outfielder Jim Wynn, field manager Luman Harris, infielder Sonny Jackson, infielder Joe Morgan, and general manager Paul Richards. *(AP Images)*

baseman Joe Morgan swatted a home run into the right field seats, a first for the new facility. The scoreboard lit up with its all-electronic "home run spectacular."*

INDOOR ARENA EXCELLENT FOR NIGHT GAMES, the *Chronicle* announced hopefully on its front page the next day. The story mentioned the previous day's troubles in the outfield and the players' complaints, but breezily went on to point out that "ball players are notoriously critical and pessimistic about the hazards of any playing conditions."[120]

That Thursday afternoon, the sun shone outside the Astrodome, and hope sprang eternal within as the players took the field for a second day of workouts. This time, the Astros' coaches came prepared with colored sunglasses in a dozen different shades for the players to try out.

The players also came prepared—they wore their batting helmets in the field.

An Astros coach stepped onto the field and started hitting practice flies to the outfielders. Sporting their new sunglasses, one by one each fielder trotted out to track the ball, then froze as he lost it in the brilliant haze of the roof. Some players would raise their glove, hoping

---
* See Chapter 15

they had guessed correctly. Most couldn't resist the natural defensive impulse to cover their head, a move that in most cases was unnecessary, as the fielder was nowhere near where the ball landed.

*Thump.* The ball would land on the grass, five feet in front of the fielder. Or ten feet behind.

"It was like looking at a million suns," recalled Astros shortstop Bob Lillis. "You just couldn't see a thing."[121]

A practice game began with the Astros facing their Oklahoma City minor-league affiliate. The first ball hit to left field landed fifteen feet in front of the fielder. *Thump.* The first hit to center fell five feet away as Oklahoma City centerfielder Ron Davis gazed helplessly at the roof. *Thump.* In fact, it was not until the third inning that any ball hit to left or center was caught. In the seventh, Mike White and Rusty Staub enjoyed back-to-back doubles on fly balls to center that dropped ten and fifteen feet away from Davis as he gazed heavenward.

*Thump. Thump.*

At the end of the seventh, Astros manager Luman Harris had had enough and called the game. "That's murder out there," said Davis, who then returned to Oklahoma with his minor league teammates. A sportswriter mused that Davis was probably thankful he hadn't made the big leagues.

There would be no more denying the problem of daylight baseball in the Dome—it was time to worry. There were indeed twenty-one day games on the Astros' 1965 schedule—a fivefold increase from the previous season when the team had avoided the worst heat in the outdoor stadium by playing only four day games at home. And more ominously, two daytime exhibition games would be played during the upcoming highly publicized opening weekend. The HSA and the architects now found themselves in a race to find a solution for day games, the first of which was to take place in less than forty-eight hours.

PART FOUR

# OPENING THE ASTRODOME

CHAPTER **FIFTEEN**

# OPENING DAY

ON FRIDAY APRIL 9, the day the Astrodome would open with an exhibition game against the New York Yankees, a banner headline on the front page of the *Houston Chronicle* declared: LBJ MAY VISIT THE DOME TONIGHT, signaling a potential triumph for Hofheinz, who had long hoped to lure his longtime crony to the premiere.

But trouble lurked directly below the headline and above the fold: a large photo of Astros outfielder Al Spangler attempting to catch a fly ball in the Dome during the previous day's practice session. Spangler, his glove raised, was squinting behind dark glasses and looking uncertainly upward, wondering where the ball might drop. On the jump page was another ignominious photo of Spangler's teammate Rusty Staub stumbling as he scrambled to pick up a fly ball that had dropped immediately in front of him.

Below the page-one photo of Spangler was another headline with more bad news: ARCHITECT SAYS HE WARNED HSA OF GLARE IN DOME. In the accompanying story, Hermon Lloyd had told newsmen he had recognized the glare problem and had warned HSA about it "months ago." Lloyd, apparently not very concerned about publicly embarrassing his client, went on to point out that his firm had not brought the problem to the attention of the stadium's owners, Harris County, having assumed that HSA would inform them. Finally, the architect speculated that the problem would best be addressed with new equipment for the players, not changes to the building: "I don't think that we will have to make any major changes in the dome...I think the answer is probably [P]olaroid sunglasses for the outfielders. Perhaps a colored baseball would help."[122] Hofheinz's reaction to all this is not recorded.

The jump pages included potential solutions—and finger pointing—interspersed with photos of Astros missing fly balls while wearing dark glasses. Since the sunglasses did not seem to work, the Astros' next hope lay with colored baseballs. The press was informed that orange, yellow, and cerise* baseballs would be used in Saturday's day game in the hope they would be more visible against the bright background. "We're busy dyeing the balls now" said an HSA publicity man.[123] In its night edition, the normally staid *Chronicle* added a lurid front-page headline: ORANGE BASEBALLS IN THE DOME!

Kansas City Athletics owner Charles O. Finley grabbed another headline by airlifting several dozen orange balls to Houston. In a telegram to Paul Richards, Finley trumpeted, YOUR PROBLEMS ARE OVER. THE A'S ARE COMING TO THE RESCUE OF THE HOUSTON ASTRONAUTS [SIC] AND THE NATIONAL GAME. SEVERAL DOZEN ORANGE BALLS ARE ON THEIR WAY. IT'S A PLEASURE TO BE OF HELP.[124] For three years, Finley had been trying to convince the major leagues to use orange baseballs, and he would continue to do so well into the 1970s. Like Hofheinz, Finley went to great lengths to introduce color into the game and believed that orange baseballs would be easier for players to see, and boost offense.[†]

At the Astrodome, preparations continued for the premiere. Hofheinz spent part of the afternoon in a golf cart, but not enjoying himself on the links; instead he drove around to every bathroom in the building to make sure each was stocked with toilet paper. A team of engineers from DuPont, manufacturers of the Lucite skylights, was flying to Houston to study the glare problem. And in a scene that must have resembled bobbing for orange, yellow, and cerise apples, another team of HSA employees huddled around vats dying baseballs for the next day's game.

---

* A moderate to deep red.
† Finley had won a 1963 rules change so his players could wear uniforms of "Kelly green" and "Fort Knox gold," and was not about to let up: "I'd like to use orange baseballs. The Army dresses our ski troops in white so nobody can see them. In baseball, we fire a white ball out of a white uniform under a bright sky. Suddenly we realize that's dangerous and make the players wear helmets. Why not use an orange baseball that everybody can see?" Michael Green and Roger Launius, *Charlie Finley: The Outrageous Story of Baseball's Super Showman,* Page 306.

Hofheinz and other Astrodome employees used golf carts to get around the building. On opening day, the Judge drove around to every bathroom in the Dome to make sure each was stocked with toilet paper. *(RGD0006, Houston Public Library, HMRC)*

During batting practice, Rusty Staub and Roger Maris amused themselves by trying to bat balls into the dome roof. Neither succeeded.[*]

In the Astrodome's gleaming control center, mechanical engineer I.A. Naman was pondering the public debut of his air conditioning system. During construction, a rumor had started, and been mentioned in the press: the Dome had skimped on air conditioning to save money.[125] Naman had realized that "people are skeptical about this thing" and decided to use the new system to send the skeptics a message. He would, as he later described it, "freeze them out the first night and there'll never be a question as to whether or not it has enough capacity." Accordingly, he instructed the operating engineers to lower thermostats throughout the building from 72 to 67 degrees. The engineers were not pleased, complaining that they had just finished the arduous task of manually setting thermostats throughout the stadium at 72. The men in the control room pushed back hard: "They'll be cold!"

---

[*] For years afterward, attempting to hit the roof became a favorite batting-practice pastime for teams visiting the Astrodome. Very few were able to do it, and no ball ever hit the roof structure during a game.

"Fine!" Naman retorted. "Let them be cold—sixty-seven degrees!"[126]

As evening fell, the first of over 47,000 spectators started to arrive, and nearly every one arrived in a car. The Astrodome was sited and built to accommodate automobiles, with 30,000 parking spaces—according to *Inside the Astrodome*, more than the entire American League—surrounding the stadium in concentric circles. Orchestrating the arrival of so many vehicles would require special attention. Long before the days of automated traffic cameras, spotters were perched atop the Dome to monitor traffic as it approached the site. The lead spotter sat in a booth at the very top of the Dome, regularly relaying updates to police on the ground up to five miles away. Two assistants were posted below him along the perimeter of the great roof.[127] Everyone scanned the flat horizon with binoculars, as if sentinels awaiting the arrival of a great mechanized army.

Back on the ground, a carload of fans approaching the Astrodome on that first big night would be in for a few surprises, beginning with the gatekeeper who genially charged fifty cents for parking.

Most male employees, whether groundskeepers, stilemen, or parking lot cashiers, were dressed in astronaut suits, complete with space helmets. Hofheinz, with his usual theatrical flair, had extended the Astrodome's space-age theme into front-line employees' uniforms. Groundskeepers, ticket takers, elevator operators, and parking lot attendants (called "Space Cadets," in the days before that term became an affectionate pejorative) wore carefully detailed blue or orange space suits and glass-front space helmets. Female ushers were dubbed "Spacettes" and wore gold lamé skirts with blue epaulettes, pillbox hats with small peek-through "windows" to match the dome roof, and blue high-heeled boots. Servers in the Astrodome's restaurants were clad in equally elaborate costumes.

The employee uniforms—costumes, really—had been created by Evelyn Norton Anderson, a wardrobe designer who worked in theater and also owned a costume and uniform company. She drew on her experience in opera and musicals, where she had learned to use colors and themes drawn from the theatrical setting. Reporting directly to Hofheinz, she had gone all out in creating the uniforms. Anderson referred to the scale of her assignment as "Wagnerian." Her coordinator

Astrodome employee uniforms designed by Evelyn Norton Anderson *(MSS1465, Houston Public Library, HMRC)*

Iris Siff was more matter-of-fact: "We were not working on a budget. We were able to select what we needed."[128]

All this had been hatched a few months earlier, in late-night meetings over cocktails at Brandt Street. At one such session, Hofheinz had convened a group to come up with names to accompany the space-themed employee costumes, and everyone was casting about for a name for the spacesuit-clad groundskeepers. Tal Smith was present at the meeting, and was beginning to think the whole thing was becoming silly. At one point, Smith sardonically suggested "why not call the groundskeepers 'earthmen?'" To Smith's surprise, Hofheinz adopted this facetious idea on the spot.[129]

Now, on opening night, the costumed front-line stadium employees were everywhere. Spacettes handed out programs, and Earthmen raked the infield. Gus Grissom, an actual astronaut who had flown in space in command of *Gemini III* just the previous month, now found himself in an elevator piloted by a Spaceman as he made his way to the Skybox Level.[130]

Of course, everyone was well dressed that night. In keeping with social norms of the times, most of the opening-night crowd arrived in their Sunday best. Men wore coats and ties, and the following day's fashion and society pages documented the women's fashions: "Mrs. Van Liew wore Samuel Winston's orange silk coat and yellow polkadot dress with pale yellow calf shoes, [and] yellow felt slouch-brim hat."[131]

Entering the stadium, your eye would naturally be drawn to the great roof and the tiers of brightly colored seats below. Hofheinz had made a point of introducing bright colors into the temporary outdoor stadium, and he insisted on the same for the Astrodome. Each tier of seats had its own color: royal blue on the exclusive ninth level, then bronze, gold, purple, black, terra cotta, burnt orange, coral, and lipstick red adjacent to the green grass. Tickets were color-coded to match the seats, making it easy to move crowds along.

Moving toward your seat, you might have noticed other amenities remarkably ahead of their time, including dedicated wheelchair spaces and designated locations where blind persons could listen to the game broadcast on the Astros Radio Network. The washroom doors were marked not with Men and Women—instead they had the respective astrological gender symbols, likely intended as another reference to space, but also providing an unintentional preview of the sexual politics of the 1970s.

The restrooms themselves were fully integrated, marking the end of the racial policies of the 1950s. Houston's hotels and remaining public facilities had been quietly and peacefully integrated in 1962. This happened partly due to pressure from the HSA, to ensure that African-Americans on visiting teams would be accommodated in the same hotels as their teammates.[132] A transition started over ten years earlier by Hofheinz was now complete.

In the restaurants, more outlandishly costumed employees waited, and they were serving more than popcorn and hot dogs. A great lover of food, Hofheinz had provided for five sit-down restaurants in the Astrodome, shrewdly spanning a wide range of price points, and each with a distinctive and frequently relentless theme. The Domeskeller was themed as a Bavarian beer garden, with plastic trees covering the structural columns, plastic elves straddling plastic beer barrels, checkered tablecloths, and waitstaff in Bavarian garb. The Countdown Cafeteria on the main level was decorated with historical sports figures and with a space-themed serving line. Overhead signs numbered each serving station as for a countdown; 10 for appetizers, 9 for entrees, 8 for sides, and so on. The all-female counter staff, dubbed Blastoff Girls, wore numbered uniforms matching the numbered signs above. The final sign—"Blastoff!"—was mounted above the cash register, with matching text on the vest worn by the cashier, who must have endured frequent ribbing. The Trailblazer offered table-service dining and a full-course meal amid a grandiose World's Fair–style historical theme (solemnly described by *Inside the Astrodome* as "depicting man's struggle for a better life down through the ages").

Posh private clubs were found on the highest levels of the stadium. The Astrodome Club was limited to season ticket holders. It offered a 100-foot-long bar as well as a "stag bar" restricted to men only. Hostesses and bartenders wore gay-nineties costumes, a favorite Hofheinz theme. The club's meat carvers were required to be males at least six-feet-two-inches tall with "imposing bearing and dignified demeanor."[133] Each wore a white, gold-buttoned coat, with one sleeve of gold-striped red velvet "to show off his carving arm,"[134] and a three-foot-tall chef's cap. Pastries were served by pretty young women dressed as French maids.

The place for Texas's Big Rich to see and be seen was the eighty-seat Skydome Club, open only to private suite-holders. In keeping with an emerging dining fad of the time, it was a replica of a Japanese steak house, with food prepared tableside by still more young women, clad in chartreuse tunics festooned with gold gamma rays. The club kept on hand for each private suite a gold spatula engraved with the suite owner's name for servings from a gourmet tray. A 210-foot-long window (in an otherwise windowless building) provided diners with panoramic views of downtown Houston, five miles distant.

But tonight the most compelling views were inside the Dome, not outside. Settling into an upholstered theater-style seat, your attention would inevitably be drawn to the vast scoreboard in center field, which was one of the Astrodome's most innovative and compelling new attractions.

The scoreboard was built around two large variable-message boards; one that displayed lineups, scoring, and statistics for the game,

The "Astrolite" screen on opening night. *(MSS1248, Houston Public Library, HMRC)*

and another for messages and out-of-town scores. These used electric matrix display technology that had been introduced in the 1950s and was increasingly replacing older, hand-operated scoreboards. The twin displays in the Astrodome scoreboard were fairly large, at 141-by-21 feet each, but were limited by technology that permitted the display of text or numerals only.

A greater innovation was the Astrolite display in the center of the scoreboard. This was a field of 10,000 lights forming a 30-by-35-foot hexagonal screen capable of displaying still and moving images with an accompanying soundtrack. Behind the scenes, the technology was crude but elaborate. Operators used conventional motion-picture and slide projectors to project films or still images onto a small light-sensitive screen comprising 10,000 photoelectric cells. The photocells were arranged to correspond with each of the 10,000 high-intensity bulbs on the big screen. It was, in essence, a colossal but primitive black-and-white television.

Most of the content displayed on the Astrolite screen was in the form of black-and-white drawings and simple animated cartoons—simple by necessity because of the low resolution of the 100-line

The 30-by-35-foot "Astrolite" screen displayed content projected onto a small light-sensitive screen backstage. Photocells on the small screen were arranged to correspond with each of the 10,000 high-intensity bulbs on the big screen. The projector at left was normally used to show photos and animated cartoons, but also for live-action features. In this 1966 view, a technician is encouraging the crowd outside to clap in unison. *(RGD0006, Houston Public Library, HMRC)*

screen. The cartoons, like all animated entertainment of the day, were produced by hand, with an average of eight drawings needed per second of viewing time. Each drawing was individually photographed by an animation camera, and then the finished film was projected onto the light-sensitive screen.

The Astrolite would display a parade of content throughout the game: batter's photos, short animated features, and even commercials, accompanied by simple sound effects. In what would become a staple of the American stadium experience, the board also acted as a cheerleader, splashing CHARGE and GO at crucial times, or simply whenever the crowd grew too quiet.

The *pièce de résistance* was the Home Run Spectacular, a light display that stretched across all of the other elements and then some, for a total length of 360 feet. It used 14,000 color Verd-A-Ray lamps, arranged not in a uniform matrix but with individual colored lamps

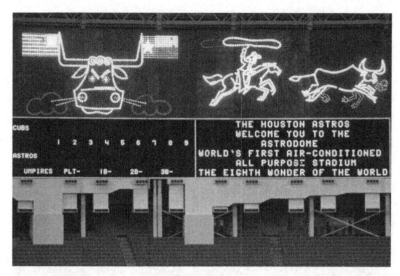

Detail of the Home Run Spectacular, above a portion of the conventional electric matrix display. *(Houston Astros)*

mounted in specific locations, forming various objects and figures. Once an Astros hit was declared a home run, the Astrolite screen would display a drawing of the hitter, and around it a preset animated sequence would begin: on the left, an illustration of the Astrodome would appear; then a baseball would burst out the roof of the dome, fly across the screen, and explode among cowboys, ricocheting bullets, and steer heads with horns sprouting the flags of the United States and Texas. The entire forty-five-second extravaganza was timed to match a runner's pace rounding the bases.

The entire ensemble stretched across 474 feet in center field—"a half-acre of information surface," gushed the commemorative program *Inside the Astrodome*. HSA paid $2 million ($15 million) to build it. Hofheinz, always seeking to control the message, had intended that there be only one sign in the stadium instead of what was then the usual patchwork of billboards plastered on the walls of other ballparks. Indeed, the only static advertising signage in the Astrodome were the giant Gulf Oil discs marking the ends of the scoreboard, the space for which Hofheinz had sold to Gulf for $1 million ($7.4 million) for five years.

The system was operated by a 25-foot console in the press area behind home plate, manned by six technicians led by a producer. Two additional operators handled the projector behind the scoreboard. Running the apparatus during games took the full crew's attention: shirtsleeved technicians hunched over blinking consoles, with the producer calling out commands as if on the bridge of a warship.

There had never been anything like it. It was, of course, all a Hofheinz concoction. He had taken his customary hands-on role in the planning, and with characteristic modesty declared the finished product "the greatest display of lights the world has ever known."[135] Like many well-known innovations, the Astrodome scoreboard synthesized a few key ideas from other ballparks—the Chicago White Sox had unveiled a crude pyrotechnic "exploding scoreboard" in 1960 and CHARGE had originated in Dodger Stadium two years later.[136] But in the Astrodome, it was all melded into a nearly continuous entertainment display that became a much-talked-about novelty.

It was, for better—or perhaps, worse—the origin of the modern sports stadium soundtrack, an experience that has since become a nearly continuous cacophony of sound and electronic visuals.

In the early days, though, there were few if any doubters about Hofheinz's multimedia extravaganza. Spectators would clap or cheer when the scoreboard prompted them, and even applaud the between-innings commercials on the Astrolite screen. Essayist Roger Angell, writing in the *New Yorker*, observed early on that the board was impossible to ignore—many Astrodome spectators watched the screen more often than they did the game.

Hofheinz loved the scoreboard, and family members referred to it as his "two-million-dollar toy." Watching games from his private box in right field, drink in hand, he would frequently pick up a gold telephone—a dedicated "hotline" connection to the scoreboard control area—to order up an Astrolite CHARGE.

In the weeks following the opener, the scoreboard would become controversial. HSA publicity director Bill Giles (son of the National League president) was put in charge of programming and operating the board. Giles put his puckish sense of humor to work with confrontational messages directed at opposing players, coaches, and umpires.

When an opposing pitcher was replaced during the game, an Astrolite cartoon depicted the deposed hurler heading for the showers, in which the water would rise over the man's head, accompanied by a funeral dirge. When a visiting manager went out on the field to argue with an umpire, a cartoon manager would be shown spouting angry gibberish.

Before long, Giles moved on to goading individuals. A favorite target was Cubs manager Leo Durocher, who had been outspoken in his criticism of the Dome, and the scoreboard itself, which he termed "bush." "Leo said a lot of negative things about the Astrodome, so every time he brought the Cubs to town, I'd kid him on the board," Giles told *Sports Illustrated* in 1972. "Once we got a rally rolling, caught up with the Cubs and finally beat them, and we flashed THIS IS THE CHICAGO FIRE, LEO." When Durocher sent his pitching coach out to the mound, the scoreboard would flash A MESSAGE FROM LEO WHO?[137]

Giles got in trouble in May, when umpire John Kibler ejected Houston players in four consecutive games. After the fourth ejection, the scoreboard flashed KIBLER DID IT AGAIN. "That's about as low as you can get, when you start putting stuff like that on the board," groused the senior umpire. "It's poor baseball ethics."[138] This was followed by a formal protest to the League president—who so happened to be Giles's father. The younger Giles reportedly replied that he would wash the scoreboard's mouth out with soap, and later recalled "in an unusual display of remorse, the next game I put I SHALL NOT WRITE MESSAGES ABOUT THE UMPIRES fifty times on the message board."[139]

Behind the scenes, sportswriters were impressed by the Dome's amenities. Arriving with their bulky manual typewriters, they were met at the stadium gate by press-box runners in orange T-shirts who would whisk the Royals and Underwoods up to the writer's designated seat in the press box. Separate dedicated press sections for baseball and football allowed each to be optimally located behind home plate and at the 50-yard line.* In other stadiums, the press boxes were usually in the open air, and the scribes normally carried wooden clothespins in their typewriter cases and used them to anchor copy paper in breezy stadiums. Inside the Astrodome, such precautions were no longer necessary. Six

---

* Early in the design stage, George Kirksey had asked the architects to investigate a rail-mounted, movable press box so that the same facility could be used for baseball and football.

darkrooms were available so that photographs could be sent via wire. Reporters enjoyed full-course meals served in a tastefully appointed dining room. Perhaps most important of all, just a few steps from the press box was the bar where a closed-circuit TV allowed journalists to plausibly do their jobs while enjoying frequent refreshments.[140]

The press-box runners did more than carry typewriters and fetch sandwiches for reporters. Hofheinz, always mindful of what the outside world was being told about Texas and Houston, handpicked the press-box staff to impress visiting journalists.

When Colt Stadium had opened in 1962, he had hired eight teenaged "ambassadors," among them fourteen-year-old Joe Siff and his twin brother Ted. The brothers had answered a full-page ad placed by Hofheinz and been quizzed on their knowledge of Houston, the United States, and baseball before being hired. Hofheinz wanted boys with sterling academic records, who were smart enough to readily answer questions from visiting reporters, and who would be, as Joe Siff recalled, "presentable to 'sophisticated easterners.'" Several "ambassadors" were class valedictorians; others were active in high school speech and debate clubs, as Hofheinz had been. They all had to be quick studies—Hofheinz required them to memorize key facts and figures about Colt Stadium and the soon-to-be-opened Dome, facts that Siff still reflexively recites nearly fifty years later. [141]

Photographers had the option of watching the game from a perch over 200 feet above the playing field by hitching a ride on an ingenious movable gondola suspended from the center of the great roof. A circular steel and glass structure 64 feet in diameter, the gondola was actually a motorized elevator that moved up and down on cables. It was primarily intended to drop down from the ceiling to provide a sound and lighting platform for smaller events such as boxing. When retracted at roof level, the gondola served as a photographers' perch with room for as many as twenty-five people. The photographers would board at field level near second base just before the game and rise slowly up to the roof as if in a hot air balloon, where they would likely remain for the full duration of the game. The gondola could not be lowered during the game, and he only other way down was via an overhead catwalk leading to the rim of the stadium. Savvy journalists learned to visit the restroom before climbing aboard.

There were other exclusive enclaves in the new stadium. Most of the 47,876 spectators that night could barely see the highest reaches of the Dome, and only a select few were admitted to the private elevators that served Level Nine. There, 107 feet above the playing field, was the domain of Houston's Big Rich. Just as he had told his daughter at their dining-room table, Hofheinz had built fifty-three "sky boxes," the first-ever examples of the luxury suites that have since become a key element in nearly every large stadium whether major league, minor league, or collegiate.

Based on Hofheinz's last-minute instructions, the plans had been revised, the structure modified, and the huge ducts relocated to a lower level. With the ducts out of the way, the suites themselves were constructed and decorated at a total cost of $1 million ($7.5 million). Those costs were paid by HSA—but not before Hofheinz sought $153,000 ($1.1 million) in county contingency funds to relocate the ductwork.[142]

Having been jammed into the space that remained, the enclosed "club rooms" that adjoined the seating area were tiny by modern standards. Each was a windowless single room measuring barely 10 by 15 feet, plus a small private bathroom. Though small in size, each was lavishly furnished and decorated in Hofheinz-inspired motifs—"Spanish Provano," "Tahitian Holiday," "Italian Gardens"— next to which "The Petroleum Room" and "Las Vegas" were tasteful in comparison. Each club room was equipped with telephone, radio, a closed-circuit television, ice maker, and a Dow Jones stock-market ticker. An elaborately costumed waiter and maitre d' were available to serve hors d'oeuvres.

Hofheinz, who fancied himself an expert in color psychology, said that he had researched and personally selected the paint colors for the sky-box level. He emphasized blue because he believed it flattering to women and went to great lengths to select shades he believed would complement their cosmetics and clothing.[143]

The fifty-three suites were leased for between $15,000 and $18,000 per year ($110,000 and $135,000). The task of selling them fell to Hofheinz's son Fred, who was working full-time for his father during that period. This role offered him an opportunity to meet Houston's movers and shakers, and helped sow the seeds for Fred's own political career.˙ He recalled, "anybody in Houston that was a wheeler-dealer, they wanted to be there."[144] The suites were snapped up by oil companies, banks, and even astronaut Alan Shepard, who had gone into business after his historic space flight four years earlier. Large corporate egos were well stroked: the company's crest was mounted prominently on the door to each suite and, of course, the engraved gold spatula was set aside for the owners' exclusive use in the Skydome Club.

Although the suites were private, Hofheinz saw that they got ample exposure in the press, starting with previews of the interior designs published in what was then called the "women's pages" of the newspapers and full-color spreads in the commemorative *Inside the Astrodome* brochure. The photos even appeared on postcards. The Judge stressed the fact that he was catering to a full spectrum of fans and price points: "We have thought of everybody, from the workingman right up to high society. For the man who wants economy we have good, low-cost meals and the only $1.50 [$11.10] pavilion seats with a cushioned bottom. And for the upper crust, we've got the club boxes on the highest level in the stadium. In the past, no baseball man has ever considered catering to the wealthy." He proudly talked about his facilities for persons "capable of paying top prices for top service, but denied that opportunity in every other stadium in the world,"[145] as if he was an advocate for disenfranchised millionaires scrounging for caviar.

More than one well-heeled visitor to the Astrodome suites found that life at the top had its drawbacks: even when seated in the front row of the suite, it was indeed difficult to make out the players on the field. In his classic essay *The Cool Bubble*, Roger Angell likened the view to that of a cattle baron viewing his prize herd from a private plane. But, all told, the game was secondary. One could readily retreat to the opulent club room, ask the red-coated butler for shrimp remoulade and a martini—and watch the game on television. Like many a high-society venue, it was not so much about the event itself as about seeing, and being seen by, one's peers.

---

˙ Fred Hofheinz was elected mayor of Houston in 1973, and served two terms (1974-77)

As if to reassure his prosperous clientele, Hofheinz liked to apply his Colosseum analogy to the private suites, explaining that in the ancient stadium "the emperor and all the bigwigs sat at the top."[146] The Judge may or may not have known that in the ancient stadium, the opposite was true: the highest levels were given over to the poorest spectators, while the emperor and important persons were seated close to the arena—where the view was better.

Beyond the clubs and sky boxes, there was another, even more exclusive, domain seen only by Hofheinz's invited guests: the lavish suite of offices the Judge had constructed overlooking right field. Any visit to these offices was memorable, regardless of whatever business was conducted. Hofheinz sat at a twelve-foot-long boomerang-shaped desk made of rosewood inlaid with black marble. This enormous desk was set on a platform that elevated him above any visitor seated across the desk. The desktop was usually clear except for a telephone, which was gold-plated and rigged to chime softly like a doorbell, as were all phones in his office and suite. The great desk was flanked by twin Bali temple guardian dogs six feet tall, carved from solid teakwood, lacquered red, and encrusted with jewels. The two beasts stared down at visitors with fangs bared. Hofheinz had picked them up on a trip to the Far East, where he said he had "bought 26,000 pounds of junk for this place. Didn't want anybody to come in here and say 'I saw the very same thing last week in Joe's bar.'"[147] Opposite the desk was less formal seating around a marble coffee table, with a gold ashtray in the shape of a baseball mitt at each corner. In subsequent years, the suite of offices would be considerably expanded.

Back on the field, Texas Governor John Connally had thrown out the first ball, and the Astrodome's first batter—Mickey Mantle—stood in at 7:48 P.M. The first pitch was a ball. The baseball was handed over to National League president Warren Giles as a memento for the Hall of Fame in Cooperstown. On the second pitch, Mantle hit a single, and the game was on.

At the start of the second inning, the PA announcer said "Ladies and gentlemen, if you will look to the box to the right of the scoreboard, you will see the *president of the United States watching the first ball game in the Astrodome!*" LBJ had indeed arrived, his entrance delayed by a bomb threat earlier. He had been pressured to make an appearance at the game by his aide Jack Valenti,* very likely at Hofheinz's urging.

A great cheer went up, and the game halted momentarily, as the scoreboard flashed WELCOME MR. PRESIDENT and the Astrolite screen displayed a portrait that, despite someone's best effort, only vaguely resembled the president. LBJ waved to the crowd, then settled in with Lady Bird to watch the game alongside Hofheinz. He watched about six innings of indoor baseball while eating dish after dish of chocolate ice cream. He was fascinated by descriptions of the electronic home run spectacular and hoped to see it in action.[148] Presumably, he and everyone else would get a chance to see it when an Astro hit a home run.

There was, however, a problem. By the eighth inning, only one home run had been hit in the game, and not by an Astro. Mickey Mantle, who had led off the first with a hit, also knocked the Dome's first homer in the sixth. Mantle walloped the ball 408 feet into the center-field stands, but, as would become customary, the scoreboard marked the opposing team's achievement with a single word: TILT.

Two innings later, President Johnson was getting ready to leave, and he had not seen the big show. Finally, Hofheinz picked up the hotline and gave the word to launch the Spectacular. Animated fireworks and pistols fired away as Mrs. Johnson watched with her mouth agape. The president wore a quizzical expression.[149] With that, the presidential party departed.

Somehow, amidst all of the Spacettes, Earthmen, electronic cowboys, and gold spatulas, a baseball game was played. The newly minted Houston Astros won that game by a score of 2 to 1 in the twelfth inning. The world's first indoor baseball game had been an unqualified success, as was the ballpark itself.

---

*Valenti was a Houston native whose advertising and PR firm had worked on the Hofheinz mayoral campaigns and gone on to a great deal of HSA work before Valenti left for Washington to join Johnson's staff. In a memo to LBJ four days before the opening, Valenti demonstrated that he had not forgotten his Houston roots nor lost his publicist's touch: "MR. PRESIDENT: The rumors about your going to Houston are based on nothing but a simple fact: This is the biggest thing that has happened in the sports world. *LIFE* (attached), *LOOK* magazine, *Sports Illustrated*, plus others, are all carrying big stories on the opening of this big domed stadium. It is the first of its kind in the world and as a result any average newspaper reporter would be inquiring if the President were going to attend since it is an unusual event which has attracted world-wide interest." Valenti closed his hyperbolic memo with an innocent-sounding coda: "I thought you would like to have this information which is the reason why reporters are asking questions." (Memo, Jack Valenti to the president, April 5, 1965, Ex TR 56, WHCF, Box 20, LBJ Library)

Another unqualified success on opening night: the air conditioning. Naman had prevailed, and convinced the building engineers to
lower the thermostats to 67 degrees. "That's damn cold," he chor-
tled as he recalled the event nearly fifty years later. Contemporary
accounts recalled women shivering beneath their husbands' jackets.[150]
A lady from Nacodoches complained to a reporter that she'd had to
wear her sweater through the entire opener: "If they could only get it
a little warmer."[151]

I.A. Naman had sent his message. There would be no more doubts
about air conditioning the biggest room in the world.

# CHAPTER SIXTEEN

# ON ACCOUNT OF SUNSHINE

THE OPENING GAME had indeed been a great success, but it had been played at night. By now, it was apparent that day games would be a serious problem. The Dome had been built to make outside weather irrelevant, but in practice it was turning out that cloudy days were needed to successfully host a baseball game.

Hofheinz put on a brave front. "Never fear," he said. "I will not be the first man to call a game on account of sunshine."[152]

Nonetheless, certain precautions were taken for the day games that followed. Astros manager Luman Harris concocted a strategy for the left and center fielders to cover each other on fly balls. Paul Richards later told reporters that Hofheinz and Smith had agreed that if conditions turned the weekend games into a farce, they would call off the game and issue refunds to every ticketholder. Richards had made arrangements with the umpires and managers to carry out this order when signaled by an announcement over the PA system.[153]

Fortunately, Houston was blessed with overcast and drizzly skies that weekend. The daytime exhibition games with the Yankees and the Orioles had a few dicey moments in the outfield but did not become a fiasco. On Saturday, Oriole Boog Powell missed a few flies. "I saw them leave the bat," Powell said after the game, "and then never saw them again." Astros outfielder Jimmy Wynn added, "If it's a cloudy day, you got a 50-50 chance of catching the ball. When it's sunny and you get that glare, there ain't no way you can catch a ball."[154] On Sunday, with the sun threatening to break through the overcast, Richards took the Yankees' manager aside and asked him to tell his infielders not to throw the ball around after each out so that the game would move as quickly as possible while it was still cloudy outside.[155]

Hofheinz and his team had dodged two bullets in the first weekend of exhibition games, but the first regular-season daytime game was scheduled for April 25, less than two weeks away. By that day, two related problems would need solutions. The first was the overpowering glare, and the second, reducing the contrast between the steel structure and the clear skylights. The colored-baseballs experiment had proved ineffective, as had the specially made extra-thick red sunglasses tested by the Astros and Orioles on Saturday afternoon.

The weeks that followed brought a frantic search for new solutions. Ralph Anderson hurriedly consulted with optometrists.[156] Back in Delaware after their emergency visit to Houston, DuPont's team of scientists tried to analyze the problem by peering at powerful searchlights shining through the acrylic.[157] Hofheinz and the HSA offices were flooded with some 1,000 letters, calls, and telegrams with unsolicited ideas to fix the problem. Some ideas came from industry: one manufacturer proposed polarized glass and another suggested a layer of translucent Kalwall suspended below the dome.

The general public also chimed in with suggestions, which, in many cases, were not quite as sensible. A lady from Massachusetts suggested beaming blue floodlights at the underside of the dome to reduce the glare. A writer from San Antonio suggested creating a "man-made eclipse" by mooring blimps over the stadium on sunny days. A man from Minnesota recommended planting vines to cover the roof, and a gentleman from Kentucky wanted to treat the ball with radium to improve its visibility.[158] Another writer advocated a less nuanced approach: "Why not take off the dome and make it a regular park?"[159]

Finally, the debacle aroused the long dormant but still cranky opposition that had argued against the bond issues to fund the Dome: "If all those jackasses who voted for the stadium would go up and sit on the roof, the stadium would be dark in no time."[160]

Having been through the mailbag, and eschewing high-tech fixes, Hofheinz turned to a simpler, time-tested idea: whitewashing the dome, as greenhouse owners had done for years to reduce sunlight in the hottest summer months. In mid-April, workmen were ordered to the roof to apply 700 gallons of an off-white acrylic paint to over 4,000 skylights. This reduced light transmission by about half, and the fielders reported improved conditions. At first, everyone believed that the problem had been solved, but as the weeks wore on, it became apparent that the paint had been only partly effective. The most blinding glare was eliminated, but in direct sunlight the white luminous surface essentially camouflaged the ball, so the fielding mishaps continued, although they were less frequent.

The final straw came on May 23 in a Sunday afternoon game against San Francisco. The Giants were at bat with two out and two on base when third baseman Jim Ray Hart hit a routine fly ball to center field. Astros fielder Jimmy Wynn trotted confidently toward the ball, but when he reached up with his glove the now-familiar story unfolded. He started to look around frantically, while the ball fell ten feet behind him. Wynn had to chase the ball all the way to the fence, allowing the Giants a two-run inside-the-park home run. In what was probably, but not certainly, a coincidence, Astros pitcher Ken Johnson, who had innocently delivered the fateful pitch to Hart, was traded in the seventh inning of that very game.[161]

Enough was enough. Hofheinz ordered up another coat of paint the following day. This second, darker coat was used on a pie-shaped wedge of the Dome behind home plate, the area that had been most troublesome to outfielders.[162] The additional paint seemed to do the trick—normal baseball could now be played. Although the roof's visual clutter of steel, sound panels and Lucite continued to present a challenge to outfielders, they found that as long as they kept their eyes steadily on the ball in flight, they could position themselves to catch it. "You can't take your eye off the ball," Willie Mays reported. "But if you watch it, you can follow it."[163]

Characteristically, Hofheinz tried to put the most positive spin on the debacle, telling a reporter that the paint was "a permanent coating that will enhance the stadium's beauty." Asked about how the lack of sunlight would affect the grass, the Grand Huckster offered a series of observations that ranged from wildly optimistic to preposterous. "We think it will continue to grow; it will require some experimentation, however, and the grass will be observed constantly by experts ... Some greenhouse experts think the paint coating will enhance the growth of the grass."[164]

The architects were probably relieved to have the embarrassing issue behind them, but as is often the case, they were more focused on how the change would affect their design. They had already compromised the roof design with the use of rectangular unit skylights instead of expressing the diamond pattern of the lamella structure; now what could have become a twentieth-century Crystal Palace was permanently sunless.

For Ralph Anderson, there was an additional disappointment, as more than three years of painstaking light-and-grass research had been rendered pointless. Anderson, who had led that effort, was bitter, writing "the client-stipulated solution, applied in haste, is a development which saddens me considerably." Writing to thank an optometry professor who had been consulted during the glare crisis, he enclosed tickets to an upcoming baseball game in the Dome, adding "This particular game is a night game so you will not have to observe the coated skylights in full light."[165]

But it was not just Anderson's feelings that were hurt. With sunlight now reduced to minimal levels, the grass itself began to die, and this time, no feat of agronomy would be able to save it. Huge patches of brown began to appear, and grew steadily. From time to time, fresh turf was brought in from the farm in Wharton to replace the dead patches, but everyone knew that this finger-in-the-dike approach could not be sustained.

Paint had solved the problems atop the Dome, and now paint would solve the problems below. For the rest of the season, the dead lawn would be painted green. Talbot Wilson recalled Hofheinz telling him that "any mistake you can correct with $20,000 [$148,000] worth of paint is no big thing,"[166] A long-term solution would have to wait until the following year.

The glare problem was finally solved, but doubts about the science of indoor baseball lingered, and in at least one case were exploited. In late April, after playing their first games in the Dome, New York Mets players complained that the Astros were manipulating the air conditioning system so that artificial breezes would blow to make the home team's hits carry farther, then reverse the cycle when the visitors came to bat. The controversy, helped along by the New York press, created quite a row in the newspapers. The fact that the Mets were one of baseball's worst-hitting teams did not escape notice. Roy Smith, the Dome's chief mechanical engineer, grumbled, "If I was capable of doing that, the Astros would be winning more games."[167]

Nonetheless, baseball commissioner Ford Frick was compelled to fly in an HVAC specialist to conduct a technical review. The specialist measured air velocity and conducted smoke-bomb tests while experimenting with various control settings on the air conditioning system. When he was done, he flatly rejected a conspiracy theory, finding that "the wind could be slightly altered in regard to direction by shutting off supply fans in various combinations, but in no case would the velocity have any effect on the action of a baseball."[168]

That ended the matter, but characteristically scoreboard impresario Bill Giles would not let a sleeping dog lie. In the following days, the scoreboard offered inside-the-Astrodome weather reports: BLOWS IN FOR THEM AND OUT FOR US.[169]

With the second coat of paint applied, and the baseball crisis averted, people around the country were taking notice of Houston and its remarkable new ballpark. In the wake of the Astrodome's apparent success, other cities rushed to consider domed stadiums of their own. Within a month of opening day in Houston, a crop of news stories about me-too designs began to pop up.

In New York, there was a $10 million ($74 million) plan to cover Shea Stadium with a dome. "Putting a dome on Shea Stadium," intoned New York Sports Commissioner Ben Finney, "is something New York must do."[170]

Even stodgy Boston entered the fray with a proposal for a domed multipurpose stadium with retractable roof. Boston's dome, perhaps by chance, would have been just two feet higher and ten feet wider than the Astrodome. It was proposed as part of a large-scale urban redevelopment project, all but unthinkable in today's Boston, but typical of the proposals across the country at the time. Under the plan, a 45-acre waterfront site would have been razed to make way for the 53,000-seat domed stadium, an adjacent arena, and thousands of parking spaces. The Boston Red Sox were quick to endorse the proposal, under which they would have vacated and sold Fenway Park.[171]

Everyone, it seemed, was watching the Astrodome, and wanted to bring baseball indoors.

Others were watching as well. Bucky Fuller and Walter O'Malley had maintained a warm correspondence for years after their collaboration in Brooklyn, and even discussed the possibility of covering a portion of Dodgers Stadium with a dome. A few months after the Astrodome opened, they exchanged pointed observations about the man they called "Judge 'H'," and the glare problems in Houston. "If [Hofheinz] had gone along with me he would not have had any optical problems and his dome would have cost less," wrote Fuller. He complained that he had consulted with Hofheinz for several years, and once the Judge had "convinced himself and others that a domed-over stadium was possible and desirable, he took on architects who immediately turned to other dome building aspirants." O'Malley replied, "...he did not follow all the 'good' advice. Mistakes were made!"[172]

O'Malley, who had a cordial but wary relationship with Hofheinz, was entitled to a small bit of snark; after all, it was he who had conceived the covered stadium concept more than fifteen years earlier. But it was Hofheinz who had actually built one, and the rest of the world was taking notice.

# CHAPTER SEVENTEEN

# CURIOSITY SEEKING

BACK IN HOUSTON, interest was as great as ever. From the day construction began, the Dome had been a magnet for curiosity seekers. Throughout construction, job meeting notes regularly mentioned provisions being made for visitors to the site, at times noting that their presence was disrupting construction activities. The contractors actually built bleachers on one side of the site, where hundreds came to gawk at the huge new structure rising from the prairie. Over 3,000 people visited the site during one week in January 1965, pushing aside barriers to get a closer look. After that, the contractors had barred all outside visitors so that they could finish their work without catering to the curious.[173] Now, with the Astrodome open and baseball season under way, a remarkable number of people wanted to visit. Of course, most came to see ball games, but many wanted only to get inside to gawk at the building itself.

A building tour program had originated as an opening week-only feature, but demand was so strong that it quickly evolved into a regular attraction. During the Astros' first road trip in April, over 5,000 people lined up to take the one-hour tour in a single weekend day, a bigger gate than some games the previous year in Colts Stadium. Four ninety-minute tours per day were conducted, all at $1.00 ($7.40) per head. About half of the tour tickets were sold to visitors from outside Harris County. The take was considerable, and Hofheinz got into a lengthy skirmish with the county commissioners when he claimed that he was not obligated to share tour revenues with the county.[174]

Behind the scenes, Hofheinz and the HSA were under pressure to book the Dome for non-baseball events. Under the terms of his lease with Harris County, the HSA had exclusive subletting rights to the stadium—a right Hofheinz needed to use to pay $750,000 ($5.5 million) in annual rent to the county, as well as $2 million ($15 million) each year for upkeep. To meet those costs, it was essential to supplement baseball income. While deals with the University of Houston and the Houston Oilers were inked or in the works, Hofheinz needed at least 125 to 150 non-baseball bookings per year in order to break even. To fill the gap, he was therefore frequently in pursuit of conventions and trade shows. "The first thing you should understand about this building," he told *Business Week* in 1964, "is that it has been planned as an auditorium in which sports events—incidentally—can be played."[175]

In early May, with the Astros headed off for a two-week, twelve-game road trip, Hofheinz rented the Dome to the local council of the Boy Scouts. Their Boy Scout Circus was a biennial event, involving hundreds of scouts from around the county. In years past the Scouts had held it in the 9,200-seat downtown Coliseum. However, the allure of the Dome was so strong that the Boy Scouts moved their 1965 Circus and—because the Astrodome rental was much more expensive—compressed the traditional three-day schedule into a single night.

A story in the *Post* said the event would include "scouting games and physical fitness, a special bicycle act, American pageantry, emergency service, camping and pioneering, Indian dancing, and a finale."[176] Perhaps not the most exciting bill of fare; it was the sort of event for which the neighbor's son might appear at your door in his uniform to sell tickets, and to be polite you would buy a few with no intention of actually showing up. However, just a month after the Dome opened, a $1 ($7.40) ticket cost less than a baseball game* and brought the prospect of a leisurely, Saturday-evening look inside the remarkable new building. Tickets started to sell briskly. The event was oversold the day before the circus, but the Scouts, expecting the usual low turnout, continued to sell tickets all day Saturday.

---

* For a family in 1965, the savings were significant: Astros ticket prices ranged from $1.50 to $3.50 ($11-$26); the Club and Skybox levels—limited to season ticketholders—cost up to $7.70 ($57).

Saturday evening finally arrived, and people started to arrive in droves. With a standing-room-only crowd of fifty thousand inside the Dome, the gates had to be closed ten minutes before showtime. Inside, it was difficult to move around—the seats were all occupied and people were standing in the aisles. On the playing field, hundreds of Boy Scouts demonstrated their outdoors skills in small groups, tying knots and applying tourniquets, all hundreds of feet away from the spectators sitting in the stands. Many parents would not have been able to pick out their sons on the field, but once again, the event itself was secondary. The building itself was the main attraction, and everyone was getting a good look inside.

Outside, however, was a different story. Thousands of ticketholders were being turned away at the entrance turnstiles, and long lines of cars were backed up bumper-to-bumper outside the parking lot. Tempers flared, and police and sheriff's deputies huddled to improvise plans to control the increasingly unruly crowd. By the time the two-hour show ended, an HSA spokesman estimated that 15,000 persons had been denied entry, and hopeful ticketholders were still driving around the parking lot, hunting for spaces.

A Boy Scout spokesman told the *Houston Post* that he was gratified by the turnout. "It's by far the biggest crowd we've ever had. It's really a sellout," he gushed, perhaps while glancing nervously over his shoulder for irate ticket holders. At a hastily arranged meeting the following morning, the scout leaders wisely decided to issue refunds.[177]

A similarly contrived Astrodome event took place at a boat show the following January. Normally, at a boat show prospective buyers purchase tickets to the hall and are free to wander among the boats, and to board larger ones. At the Astrodome's Skipper's Jamboree and Preview, the boats themselves sat on trailers on the playing field (which, by that time, was unpainted dirt), and for whatever reason, ticket holders were not permitted on the field. Instead, they sat in the stands and squinted at the boats from hundreds of feet away while an announcer described the features of each craft. The event was spiced up with live country music and a Miss Mermaid contest. The pretty young "mermaids" posed on the boats during the sales pitches, leaving many prospective skippers wishing they had brought their binoculars.

After the one-night Astrodome Preview, the boats were hauled off to the Sam Houston Coliseum downtown, where the actual six-day boat show took place, and buyers were finally able to walk in to slam the hatches and kick the gunwhales.

It was in retrospect more than a little bit silly, but no matter. Getting a close look at the boats could wait. The big attraction was the Astrodome. Coupled with the popularity of Hofheinz's dollar-a-head daytime tours, these episodes demonstrated that the Dome itself was becoming a regional attraction, no matter which act was booked inside.*

In the spring of 1965, the brown grass was the only blemish marring the Astrodome's success. The turnstiles were clicking at record-high numbers. On home-game weekends, nearby hotels were full of tourists who had driven from out of town and out of state to gawk at the Dome. The days of walking up to the box office on game day and getting a good seat were a distant memory.

Even the Astros, an expansion team that had posted losing records in its first three seasons of existence, were getting hot. They won ten straight games in late April, and Hofheinz, tongue perhaps in cheek, fretted over a potential World Series conflict. "We may have a real problem," he told a reporter. "If we get into the World Series whatever will we do with Billy Graham?"[178] Graham, an evangelical Baptist who routinely drew thousands for his multiday Crusades held in large arenas, had been booked into the Dome for mid-October.†

There was heady talk of even greater spectacles, such as staging Verdi's *Aida* in the Dome, with a cast of 10,000 and Texas's three symphony orchestras playing simultaneously.[179] The sky, or perhaps the steel dome overhead, was the limit.

---

* The Astrodome continued to draw visitors for years. By 1973, the Dome hosted 420,000 tours annually, and the following year a survey by the U.S. Commerce Department found that the Astrodome was the third most popular man-made tourist attraction in the United States. The Dome had been edged out only by the Golden Gate Bridge and Mount Rushmore, and beat humbler efforts such as the Statue of Liberty and Hoover Dam. ("There's More Texas Than Technology in the Houston Astrodome," *New York Times*, April 7, 1974; "Astrodome No. 3 in U.S. As Tourist Attraction," Associated Press story in *Houston Chronicle* 1/10/1974)
† The Astros averted this scheduling dilemma by finishing their season at 65-97, ninth place in the National League and 32 games behind the Dodgers.

CHAPTER **EIGHTEEN**

# CONVERSION

WITH THE SUNLIGHT PROBLEMS SOLVED and baseball season off to a promising start, it was time to look ahead to the 1965 football season. The HSA had been formed to attract other sports along with baseball, and the Astrodome had been designed to accommodate both football and baseball. The Dome was one of the earliest examples of a multipurpose stadium, perhaps better described as a baseball park that could readily be converted for football.

In theory, designing a baseball stadium that could be shared with a football team was an eminently sensible idea. Professional football in those days was still lagging well behind baseball in popularity, and football teams played only a handful of games each season. The purpose-built, pro football stadium now commonplace across America was virtually nonexistent in the early 1960s. Most pro football teams were tenants in college football stadiums and major league baseball parks. In the early 1960s, the New York Giants played their home games in Yankee Stadium, while the Boston Patriots performed at Fenway Park.

In practice, the incompatible geometries of football and baseball produced configurations that were not ideal for either sport but workable, and the efficiency of a shared facility was attractive to local governments struggling to finance stadiums.

The Astrodome had been designed with movable sections of stands that could be rotated approximately 35 degrees to face the baseball foul lines or the gridiron sidelines as needed. The technology had recently been pioneered at new stadiums in Washington, D.C., and New York City. The 5,000-seat movable sections were mounted on steel wheels

set on rails, and were hauled back and forth with ten-horsepower mo-
tors.* The conversion process took about two hours, most of which
was spent removing and resetting the natural turf sections atop the
rails and below the stands.

For the Astrodome, football was intended to provide another
source of rental income. The University of Houston Cougars had already signed on as a football tenant, and Hofheinz had what was described as a "gentlemen's agreement" on a sublease with Bud Adams,
owner of the Houston Oilers of the American Football League, an
organization still in its infancy. Adams had been an HSA stockholder
in earlier days and was a founder of both the AFL and the Oilers.
Like most other pro football teams, the Oilers did not have a stadium
to call their own, and were tenants in Jeppesen Stadium on the University of Houston campus. As the time approached to formalize the
"gentlemen's agreement," it became apparent that the gentlemen had
much different recollections of just what was in the agreement.

This clash of memories turned into a high-profile feud that boiled
over into the press during the spring. The *Houston Chronicle* ran a full-
page spread filled with excerpts of the legal language from each side's
proposed version of the lease. Hofheinz challenged Adams to a televised
debate on the subject, an invitation that Adams wisely declined.[180]

Hofheinz, always a tough negotiator, had met his match in Adams,
a wealthy oilman who handed out gas station franchises as bonuses
to his top players. In June, Adams announced that he had reached an
agreement for the Oilers to play their 1965 home games in Rice Stadium. Hofheinz publicly left the door open for Adams to change his
mind, but could not resist taking a swipe at his opponent: "I feel sorry
for Bud's fans who had to walk across muddy parking lots and sit on
hard wooden benches in the rain for five years. They did so in good
faith because they thought Bud was going to move into the Dome."[181]

---

* Other cities grappled with the same problem in the early 1960s, and at least one considered
a more novel solution. In San Diego, one proposal would have sited its sports complex on the
shores of Mission Bay, with baseball and football fields on adjacent plots of dry land. The plan
called for massive floating sections of grandstands to be built and towed to whichever field was
needed for that day's game. (Wells Twombly, "Trend In Stadiums" *Houston Chronicle*,
January 20, 1965)

But Adams stuck to his guns and moved his team to Rice, leaving Hofheinz without a major tenant. Football came to the Dome on September 11, 1965, when the University of Houston opened their 1965 football season, but the Astrodome would be idle on Sunday afternoons that fall, and for the next two seasons as well. The Judge made moves to secure a football franchise for himself in the rival National Football League, but NFL rules prohibited a baseball team owner from owning an NFL franchise. The Dome would not see a professional football game until Hofheinz and Adams finally came to terms in 1968.

Hofheinz was bruised by the spat with Bud Adams, and as that controversy reached its peak in the spring of 1965, Hofheinz suddenly found himself fighting a two-front war. He would soon become embroiled in another high-profile dispute, one with even greater stakes, and a more formidable opponent.

# CHAPTER NINETEEN

# THE MASTER
# OF THE ASTRODOME

CRAIG CULLINAN HAD BEEN THE FIRST TO GO.

He had helped launch the HSA, and had spent a great deal of money and his own sweat equity pounding the pavement alongside George Kirksey in the hunt for a major league team. Their quest was a success, but by 1962, Cullinan realized that he had made a big mistake. Although he had the means to purchase most of the stock in HSA, he had stood by while Smith and Hofheinz acquired two thirds of that stock, and with it control of the organization. Cullinan, heir to a Texas oil fortune, was left as a minority stockholder. As time passed, he grew uncomfortable with Hofheinz's increasing power and meddling in baseball operations.[182] Cullinan had become involved with the HSA as a civic gesture; his interest in baseball was really more about the crack of the bat than about financial reward. After the 1962 baseball season, he pulled out and sold his stock to Smith. It was an amicable parting, and in later years Cullinan was spotted in the Astrodome stands from time to time. But he remained an outsider.

Smith and Hofheinz now held 80% of the stock, and Hofheinz, with Smith's tacit blessing, was firmly in control. The two men went back many years. They'd first met during World War II, when Hofheinz was county judge and Smith, already a millionaire, held a dollar-a-year post as the city's director of civil defense. In all the years since, Smith had stuck with his friend through thick and thin. He had been a staunch supporter of Hofheinz during his mayoral elections as well as his tussles with the city council. In an oft-repeated story about the 1955 election, Smith was getting a haircut in a downtown barbershop when another patron made an insulting comment about Hofheinz. Smith, the story goes, leapt from the barber's chair and asked the man if he might like a punch in the nose, then chased him out of the shop.

After Hofheinz lost the election that year, the two became business partners, and Smith gave Hofheinz considerable leeway in investing his fortune. In the late 1950s, as the HSA moved toward acquiring a major league franchise, it was Smith who brought the Judge into the group and gave him an option to buy a third of the stock. As recently as April 1965, Smith had described Hofheinz as "the best friend I've ever had."[183]

But his view changed the following month, when the newspapers began reporting that the two were abruptly ending their business relationship. It appeared that like Cullinan, Smith had grown disillusioned with the Judge's management style. Smith later said publicly that Hofheinz was "just too autocratic," and news stories hinted at other tensions. Some said that Smith and his wife resented the Judge's propensity for grabbing headlines, and it had not escaped notice that when LBJ visited the Dome on opening night, the Smiths had not been invited to Hofheinz's box to meet the president until the seventh inning.

Now, for whatever reason, Smith had had enough of Hofheinz, and he presented the Judge with an ultimatum: "You buy me out or I'll buy you out." Under the terms of their partnership agreement, Smith had to give the Judge ninety days to put up funds to buy Smith's share of the stock. If Hofheinz couldn't come up with the money, he was indeed out. Smith told reporters that with Hofheinz gone he would "get me a man in there to run it right, even if I have to pay him $200,000 ($1.5 million) a year."[184] However, if Hofheinz did raise the funds, Smith would be obligated to sell and be left with only a small percentage of the stock.

Smith almost certainly expected to emerge in control of the team, and conventional wisdom at the time was on his side. To buy Smith's share, Hofheinz would need to raise a lot of money—reportedly $7.5 million ($55 million). The Judge was a wealthy man, but unlike Smith, he did not have the means to simply write a check for that amount.

Over the summer, Hofheinz began taking steps to raise the money. He moved out of his large home and into a hotel, freeing the home and property to be used as collateral. He also mortgaged his stake in a television station.[185] But it wasn't enough, and he went out in search of bank financing, reportedly from as far away as Amsterdam.

Over the following months, relations between the two men continued to deteriorate. There were reports of shouting matches in the HSA offices. In July, Hofheinz infuriated Smith by changing the locks on the Astrodome—one day the formidable tycoon found that his keys no longer worked. Soon after, Smith told reporters, "All this talk about everything being friendly between us is just not true. We're not...There's no such thing as a friendly relationship between him and me."[186]

Hofheinz put on his usual brave face, but the stakes were enormous and it was an extraordinarily tense situation. He later told a friend he had been unable to sleep during that period; the episode was one of few in his life in which the Judge had confronted fear of failure.[187]

But he did not fail. By August, the Judge surprised many with the news that he had raised the money and was able to exercise the option. He now held over 80 percent of the stock, and with it undisputed control of the HSA and the Astros.

Although Smith still held 10 percent of the HSA stock, he was left on the outside looking in. He was compelled to resign as chairman of the board. In media interviews, he left no doubt that he would never collaborate with Hofheinz again, but graciously acknowledged the Judge's leadership in creating the Astrodome. "I'll give him credit," he told an interviewer. "Of course, give him time and he'd take it anyway."[188]

General manager Paul Richards' was the next head to roll. Richards had at least known what he was getting into. At his first press conference the day he was hired in 1962, he had been asked how long he would be general manager in Houston, and he replied "Right up to the day that the Judge decides he knows more about baseball than I do." That day arrived in December 1965, when Hofheinz called a press conference to announce that Richards was being fired. To console Richards after the press conference, a small group of friends took him out to a hotel bar, where Kirksey told him "The

Judge is his own worst enemy." Richards took a drink and replied: "Not while I'm alive."[189]

Of the original HSA core group, George Kirksey was the last man standing, and his future prospects were not promising. In the early years of the HSA, Kirksey had correctly assumed that Hofheinz and Smith would eventually battle for control of the ballclub. He had aligned himself with Smith and Richards, assuming that wealth and baseball knowledge would triumph. Like many observers of the Hofheinz-Smith dispute, Kirksey had assumed Hofheinz would not be able to raise the money, and that Bob Smith and his fortune would triumph in the end.[190]

As it turned out, Hofheinz had outfoxed the tycoon, and then dismissed the baseball wizard. Kirksey had picked the wrong horse, and Hofheinz was not inclined to overlook it. In November, a rare letter from Hofheinz notified Kirksey that his contract would not be renewed the following year. "Future agreements between ourselves will have to be negotiated from the beginning,"[191] the letter said, leaving little doubt that there would be no such future agreement. Still holding 2 percent of the HSA's stock, Kirksey hung on through the off-season but was left with little to do as he was moved to a smaller office and stripped of his executive vice president title. In May, he had had enough and agreed to sell his stock to Hofheinz. "It has been an illuminating experience,"[192] Kirksey said as he ended his sixteen-year baseball adventure and cleaned out his desk. Pocketing a reported $175,000 ($1.26 million), he announced that he was going to buy a sports car and tour Europe.*

Just six years earlier, Hofheinz had been asked to join a small group of boosters trying to build a stadium and land a baseball team. Now the others were gone, but the stadium was built, and Hofheinz stood alone as head of HSA and master of the Astrodome.

---

* Kirksey did indeed buy a sports car and tour Europe, and unfortunately he was killed in a 1971 accident at the wheel of his Porsche, in France.

# CHAPTER TWENTY

# UNDERTAKER'S GRASS

LATE IN THE SUMMER OF 1965, Tal Smith was under more than a little pressure. The thirty-one-year-old Massachusetts native had spent most of his career in baseball, beginning in the front office of the Cincinnati Reds, a protégé of general manager Gabe Paul. In 1960, when Paul was hired as the first general manager of the new Houston franchise, Tal had made the move with him. Paul grew frustrated working under Hofheinz and soon resigned, but Tal decided to stay behind—he liked Houston, and had a good relationship with Hofheinz. As time went on, Tal found he did not much like his new boss, Paul Richards, and was having trouble getting along with him. Relations between the two gradually deteriorated, with the usual outcome in such situations: in early 1963, Tal learned he was being let go.

As he cleaned out his office and said his goodbyes, he was approached by the Judge. Hofheinz apologized for what had happened, but added, "I can't do anything about it. We need [Richards] right now. But I don't want you to go,"[193] and he asked Tal to stay on as his representative on the Dome project. Tal was skeptical at first—he was a front-office baseball man with no training as an architect or engineer. But Hofheinz had an eye for talent, and his offer stood. Tal accepted it.

By this time, construction was well underway, and in his new role Tal had had to learn quickly about putting a building together and dealing with arcana like electrical drawings and door schedules. Recalling those early days, he said, "It was sink or swim, and I learned on the job."[194]

Now, as Tal surveyed the completed Astrodome two years later, the grass on the field had died and was being repainted regularly. One day, Hofheinz told him, "Tal, I don't care what you have to do—find a solution to this. You've got whatever you need."[195]

Tal pushed his other work aside, and concentrated on the grass issue. The baseball-man-turned-construction-manager now found himself moving into yet another unexpected occupation—research and development for indoor playing surfaces. By this time, the story had gained national media attention, and the HSA started to receive all sorts of inquiries, unsolicited suggestions, and product proposals. Tal met with salesman after salesman and listened to pitches for carpet and other flooring materials, many of which were hard surfaces that did not simulate grass at all. He also heard pitches about chemicals that could be applied to the grass to help it grow, and others to color it. His office soon filled up with samples of carpet, rubber flooring, paints, and lawn chemical products, but after weeks Tal had seen "nothing that warranted a second look."

Then he received a call from Providence, Rhode Island. The caller was Dick Theibert, athletic director at Brown University, and he was calling to invite Tal to Providence to see a new artificial turf product that had been installed at a private school a few blocks from the Brown campus. Tal was about to get his first look at what would become known as AstroTurf.

In the twenty-first century, AstroTurf remains a trademark and a robust commercial product, which, like many successful brands, has evolved into a generic term for a number of similar products produced by many different companies. More recently, the word itself has also become a pejorative, referring to artificially produced popular political advocacy—a perversion of "grassroots"—or evoking artificiality in general.

Artificial turf, however, was born out of the idealism of the 1960s at Educational Facilities Laboratories (EFL), a nonprofit think tank that conceived and tested various innovations in school buildings. EFL and its highly regarded founder, Dr. Harold Gores, were responsible for a wave of progressive ideas such as open-plan schools, moveable interior partitions, and language labs, as well as improved creature comforts such as air conditioning and carpeting. Backed with ample funding from the Ford Foundation, EFL not only generated the ideas, it provided the capital needed to develop some of the most promising ones.

One of Gore's pet projects was an effort to address inequities in physical fitness by improving urban school playgrounds. At the time, outdoor play space was particularly lacking in inner-city schools, where the "playgrounds" were often small patches of blacktop surrounded by chain-link fence and, due to space constraints, frequently located on the roof. Gores sought a way to create synthetic grass that would encourage vigorous play and reduce injury. The surface would need to be low-maintenance, mold- and mildew-resistant, colorfast, and resilient. A 1961 EFL report stated a goal of inventing "a material that looks like grass and acts like grass, a turflike substance on which a ball will bounce and a child will not, a covering that brings a slice of spring in Scarsdale to 14th Street in April."[196] The comparison of New York's leafy suburbs and its working class downtown neighborhoods suggests that EFL hoped for a solution that would address social justice along with physical fitness.

Meanwhile, the Monsanto Chemical Company, at the time an industrial chemical and plastics behemoth, was seeking a foothold in consumer products by producing and marketing synthetic fibers for consumer products such as clothing and carpeting. To this end, Monsanto had launched a new research and development company, the Chemstrand Corporation. By the early 1960s Chemstrand had developed a high-density nylon ribbon that could be woven into carpet. It was a key breakthrough: traditional carpet fibers were relatively thin, and tended to retain rainwater. The new nylon material was durable, water-resistant, and colorfast. Gores reached out to collaborate with Chemstrand, and soon became engrossed in the problem, bringing home samples and tinkering with swatches of rubbery material.[197]

Chemstrand (which was eventually absorbed completely into Monsanto) dubbed its new product Chemgrass, a name that sounds odd today but chemistry was, at that time, a symbol of progress and a positive branding attribute. In those days, Monsanto's industry rival DuPont used "Better Living Through Chemistry" as a marketing tagline, and sponsored a Wonderful World of Chemistry pavilion at the 1964 World's Fair.

Chemgrass, as a first-generation product, was still in the testing stages and not yet available for purchase when in 1964, EFL underwrote a $200,000 ($1.5 million) test installation in a field house at the Moses Brown School in Providence, Rhode Island. Moses Brown, an elite private school for boys, was perhaps not the inner-city schoolhouse envisioned by Gores, but the school's headmaster had ties to the Ford Foundation and successfully lobbied to make his school the test bed. The synthetic turf had been in place for about a year at Moses Brown when Theibert (who also had Ford Foundation ties) called Houston in the fall of 1965.

In August 1965, Tal Smith and one of the architects flew to Providence to take a look for themselves. Theibert met them and took them to the field house. The new turf had been laid in the center of an asphalt oval running track, and under the field house lights, its vivid green color was striking in contrast to the black asphalt. The Houston men carefully walked over the turf. They bounced balls off the surface and threw ground balls to one another. Smith recalled, "It felt good, it looked good, and the ball seemed to react alright."[198]

Tal returned to Houston with a positive report for Hofheinz. Perhaps gazing at the dead grass in his outfield, Hofheinz asked for a meeting with Monsanto. Referring to himself as the Astrodome Research Corporation, the Grand Huckster graciously offered Monsanto the use of the Astrodome as a second test bed and somehow convinced the company to pay for the material and installation. Naming rights were part of the deal—Hofheinz, who had been trying to protect *Astro* as a marketing prefix, agreed that Monsanto would call its product AstroTurf.[199]

Over the following months, Monsanto struggled to refine and accelerate production of the material at its plant in Pensacola, Florida—at the time, the only location where the nylon fiber was manufactured. By January 1966, they had produced and installed enough material to cover the Astrodome infield, and one evening Hofheinz called in a few Astros after hours to give it a try.

The material had been laid in strips, with the seams sealed with over three miles of zippers. The seams were set parallel to a line drawn from home plate through second base. The ballplayers found that balls hit in the infield behaved very strangely—a ball hit toward shortstop would hop, then veer toward third. Someone decided to try hitting from different directions, and found that when the ball was hit from third base toward first—across the seams— the problem disappeared. The turf, it turned out, had what was called a "tilt": due to the manufacturing process, all of the short and stiff nylon ribbons lay in the same direction on any roll of turf.[200] When the ball traveled parallel to the tilt, it behaved more or less normally.

When the turf was pulled up, turned 90 degrees, and reinstalled, the problem vanished. Hofheinz announced himself satisfied and ordered up another infield installation to be completed for an exhibition game scheduled for March.

Monsanto's management was reluctant. The technology, while promising, was still in development, and the company prudently believed that more testing was needed. Hofheinz would have none of it. "We must try it. I have a season coming up and I can't live with what I've been living with, and I think it will work and that's what we're going to do."[201] The company acquiesced and mounted a crash effort to produce a second infield* in about ten weeks' time. They worked down to the wire, completing installation at about 2:30 A.M. on game day, March 19.

Returning to the Dome later that day, the Monsanto men were surprised to find that Hofheinz had cut the first infield into six-inch squares and was selling them in his gift shops for $1 ($7.40) apiece.

As at the Moses Brown field house the previous year, many were impressed by the new turf's color—it was, in the words of one witness, "as pure a green as you'll find on the most beautiful golf course in the world."[202] It was a striking complement to the rainbow of seat upholstery in the Dome.

The color, of course, was artificial—the nylon ribbon could be produced in just about any color, and for the Astrodome, green had not been a foregone conclusion. Hofheinz, as always striving for maximum visual impact, had considered a range of colors that were decidedly nothing like grass. In one of his more unnerving schemes, the turf would have been blue in the infield, yellow in the outfield, and

---

*The company could not produce enough material to cover the outfield until later that year.

The Astrodome's new artificial turf was touted as the first playing surface ever to be vacuumed, and between innings that became part of the show. Note that this "earthman's" vacuum cleaner is not connected to power. *(Houston Astros)*

red along the foul lines. In a rare concession to conventional wisdom, the Judge had settled on green because people were more accustomed to it.[203]

The first game played on artificial turf was, to everyone's relief, largely routine baseball. Everyone noticed, however, that the field was *very* fast—the synthetic surface was more resilient than planted soil, and batted balls retained more of their energy when bounced off the field. After the game, the engineers gathered on the field with Hofheinz. One mused that it would be possible to adjust the substrate to slow down the ball—in other words, to make it behave more like grass. Hofheinz glared at him and said, "Forget about it son. Give me nothing but three-base hits."[204]

The turf made its debut to remarkably good reviews from ballplayers, particularly from the Astros, who had performed on painted dead grass for most of the previous season. Its man-made precision eliminated divots and bad hops. Everyone learned to adjust to the high bounces and to wear rubber-soled shoes instead of metal spikes for traction. The spacesuit-clad Earthmen made a great show of vacuuming the turf between innings. AstroTurf and its scientific parentage was also well received in the press—it was, according to the *New York Times*, "a blue-green triumph of chemistry."[205]

Other teams rushed to follow suit. Within just five years, artificial turf was rolled out in seven major-league ballparks; by the 1971 season, one in four baseball games was played on carpet. Sportswriters of the day advocated for its adoption at all ballparks. Philip K. Wrigley, owner of the Chicago Cubs, a traditionalist who had refused to hold night games in his ballpark, made plans to replace his grass with AstroTurf. Synthetic turf's market share continued to grow for years afterward.[206]

In later years, concerns would emerge about artificial turf: it was suspected of causing new types of injuries, and became known for heat gain that roasted outfielders in outdoor parks. Eventually, there was pushback on the "artificiality" of it all. But in the 1960s, it was difficult to find critics of artificial turf. In fact, in those days its greatest drawback was low profitability. It took seven years for Monsanto to make money on its new high-profile product.

The commercial application that finally moved AstroTurf into the black was not in vast new stadiums or inner-city playgrounds—it was the iconic AstroTurf doormat with the white daisy sprouting in the corner that plopped onto millions of American doorsteps beginning in 1969.[207] Monsanto, via the Astrodome, had finally found its way into the consumer market.

CHAPTER **TWENTY-ONE**

# THE JUDGE'S QUARTERS

SOON AFTER THE ASTRODOME OPENED IN 1965, Hofheinz found himself without a place to live. To raise cash to fund the Bob Smith buyout, he had mortgaged his 80-acre home west of Houston. Under state law he could not use his homestead as collateral, so he had to vacate the property, and he had moved into a hotel. The following year Dene Cafcalas Hofheinz, the Judge's wife of 33 years, died. Shaken, he moved into his Astrodome office suite, which had a bedroom on an upper level. Shortly afterward, he decided to enlarge the two-story suite into a five-story residence that spanned a narrow, curved segment of the stadium along the right field wall and behind the scoreboard. Hofheinz had created the Astrodome, and now he would make it his home.

Houston architects designed the Astrodome, but for his expanded office and personal quarters, Hofheinz brought in out-of-town design talent. Harper Goff was an artist and production designer for film and the stage. Goff is best known for his collaborations with Walt Disney: he was production designer for Disney's 1954 film adaptation of *20,000 Leagues under the Sea* and is credited with the conceptual development of Disneyland attractions such as the Jungle Cruise and Main Street USA.[208]

Hofheinz, who loved themed environments, had found his man in Goff, a set designer of considerable talent who quickly figured out what this particular client was looking for. "I knew what he wanted— flamboyant," Goff would later say,[209] and he set out to decorate a suite of rooms behind the right-field wall in a space five floors high and 200 feet long but only 26 feet wide.

Goff roamed the country with the Judge seeking antique furnishings for the suite, which was of course lavishly decorated but also filled with quirky amenities and gimmicks. The suite included a billiard parlor, a six-hole miniature golf course (carpeted, of course, in Astroturf), a one-seat barbershop, a beauty parlor (for the use of Hofheinz's daughter Dene), a shooting gallery, and a bowling alley. Hofheinz also installed a nursery and children's play area, which included an Astrotot Puppet Theater in which Hofheinz staged plays for his grandchildren. The Judge's adult guests could watch the action on the field from a balcony, while the grandchildren watched the game through small windows nearby, each set at the child's own height. "He thought of *everything*," his daughter Dene Hofheinz Anton recalled.[210]

Nearby was a chapel, clad in faux stone and stained glass. The chapel, planned for Dome-related activities such as ballplayer weddings, was interdenominational by virtue of interchangeable religious fixtures—a cross could be quickly replaced with a Star of David, or even a torii, the symbolic wooden gate of Shintoism.

The dining room was a balcony overlooking right field, themed as a New Orleans-style "French Kitchen," complete with cast-iron railings and trim. A photo spread in a 1969 magazine profile pictured Hofheinz and his new wife (he had married his longtime secretary earlier that year) on this balcony enjoying a meal on fine china, with the vast, empty stadium beyond. In the photo, Hofheinz holds his wife's hand in his, along with a cigar.[211]

Hofheinz's sense of humor showed in several elaborate practical jokes built into the suite. Goff devised a novelty barroom, dubbed the Tipsy Tavern, which had a floor tilted at a 20-degree angle and tables bolted to the floor. A similarly skewed window looked out onto the stadium. The end of the bar was fitted with a large concealed electromagnet. When a person seated at the end ordered a beer, the bartender—frequently Hofheinz himself, or someone else who was in on the gag—would reach for a special beer stein which was discreetly fitted with another magnet. He would fill it with beer, then quickly slide it down the bar. Seeing the large glass full of beer hurtling toward him, the "mark" would frequently leap out of the way, only to find

The Astrodome's interdenominational chapel. *(Houston Astros)*

that the stein abruptly and neatly stopped at the edge of the bar. The bartender used a foot pedal to activate the concealed electromagnet.

Flipping another concealed switch would cause one of the barstools to rise very slowly. During one of his trademark late-night calls, Hofheinz had engaged his chief engineer to fit it with a pneumatic lift so that the rise would begin gradually, unnoticed by the mark until he stumbled when he tried to get off the stool.[212]

A visitor to the bar who asked to use the restroom would be directed to an elevator. As he entered it, the door would close and the floor of the cab would start to vibrate. A brick wall visible through a small window would accelerate and start to speed by, lending the illusion that the elevator cab was moving down, while in reality it remained stationary. A door on the other side of the cab would then open, revealing a dank space filled with cobwebs and leaking pipes. In the center of the room was a large barrel with a hose leading from the bottom. A sign on the barrel read WHEN FINISHED USING TOILET, PLEASE RELEASE A SMALL AMOUT OF WATER. At that point, the gag would be called off, and the mark directed to a proper restroom.[213]

A portion of the area was set aside for a two-floor Presidential Suite. A VIP entering it would encounter a two-story foyer and drawing room decorated in Louis XIV and XV furniture, tapestries, and artwork. A circular carpet bearing the presidential seal (permission for the use of which was said to come from President Johnson himself) sat at the base of a winding stair that led upstairs to the presidential bedroom, guest rooms, and two princess-style bedrooms for Johnson's daughters. The suite also included a communications center (in which, according to Goff, "the red telephone would be located"[214]). The suite was built at least in part because Hofheinz had hoped to lure both 1968 political conventions to the Dome and felt that the suite would be an important amenity. But above all, Hofheinz prized his relationship with Johnson. Goff later said, "He was always thinking of Lyndon Johnson and his family."[215]

Downstairs, in an obscure storage area below the suite, Hofheinz kept his collection of antiques, sculpture, paintings, and curios gathered over years of travel. He took visitors on tours to see his various acquisitions, such as rickshaws and pedicabs from Asia, nineteenth-century furniture, and a grand piano inlaid with mother of pearl.[216]

It was all "flamboyant" indeed—to put it politely. Hofheinz characterized the lavish suite as a sales tool necessary to attract convention business. As always, his primary sales tactic was to leave a strong impression with potential customers. His daughter Dene said, "He wanted them to be overwhelmed by [the suite] and he wanted them to leave there talking about it,"[217] just as pedestrians in downtown Houston forty years earlier would have talked about seeing young Roy dressed in a clown suit, with a giant yo-yo in one hand and a billy goat in the other. The Judge felt that if you could not sell in this business-entertainment mecca, you couldn't sell anywhere.

There is little question, however, that Hofheinz, who clearly craved the trappings of wealth, was building for himself as well. Many visitors found it all too gaudy, but Hofheinz reveled in it. As Goff told *Sports Illustrated*, "When hoity-toity people came in and whispered about the bad taste, he loved it."[218]

The Judge happily settled into his new home, but the new residence marked a turning point in his life. After the death of his first wife, the Judge's health had declined, and he started gaining weight. Fred Hofheinz recalled that around this time, his father withdrew and became somewhat reclusive, not emerging from his Dome quarters for long stretches. "I've spent more than a week in here without ever seeing daylight," Hofheinz told a reporter in 1968. "I try now to get out every day or two."[219]

Outside the Astrodome, other improvements were underway. As he sat in the suite, the Judge was making preparations to construct a small empire.

CHAPTER **TWENTY-TWO**

# THE RISE AND FALL OF THE ASTRODOMAIN

*"This is only the beginning. The domed stadium will become to Houston what the Leaning Tower is to Pisa and what the Eiffel Tower is to Paris. It will be hard to equal."*

—JUDGE HOFHEINZ[220]

FROM THE VERY BEGINNING, Hofheinz had seen the Astrodome as the centerpiece of a vast convention and entertainment complex. Aware that most visitors to the Dome came from outside Harris County, he wanted more than one opportunity to access those visitors' pockets. He told a reporter, "Most people have no vision. They'll build a Coney Island and quit. Or a race track and quit. Or they'll get a pro football team and quit. I intend to pull them all together here."[221]

With the Dome now complete, Hofheinz moved to assemble that new complex, using land he had shrewdly assembled adjacent to the site. The Astrohall Exhibition and Convention Center was completed the year after the Dome opened. With 500,000 square feet of exhibition space, it was by 1968 the largest such facility in the world, positioned to attract national trade shows. Astrohall included a roof that unmistakably resembled a circus tent, another Hofheinz tribute to the Big Top, and one that the Judge would soon outdo: in 1967 he and a partner purchased the Ringling Brothers Barnum & Bailey Circus.

Astroworld USA, opened in 1968 on a sixty-acre site south of the Dome complex, was an amusement park heavily influenced by Disneyland, and the attractions at the 1964 New York World's Fair. As always, the Judge's touch was evident throughout the park in a succession of themed areas: Americana Square, Western Junction, and the Mexican Fiesta Plaza. Families could ride an alpine-themed rollercoaster through the caverns of der Hofheinzburg, or take in the view from the top of the 340-foot Astroneedle. A distinctly Houstonian feature of the new park was a 2,000-ton outdoor air conditioning system, used to cool picnic and waiting areas.

By 1969, what was to become the capstone of the empire was in place with the completion of the Astroworld Hotel/Motel complex west of the Dome. Hofheinz managed to assemble franchises of four competing hotel chains on a single site, and operated them under a single reservation system. The top floor of the flagship Astroworld Hotel was given over to the Celestial Suite, designed by Harper Goff. It featured antiques from Hofheinz's own collection, and, of course, his characteristic lavish finishes and interior-decoration themes: a Madrid Castle living room, a P.T. Barnum Circus Suite, a Fu Manchu Room, and Tarzan's Adventure Suite, complete with rope swing. Its centerpiece was a two-story Minidome Room nightclub, a miniature duplicate of the Astrodome, complete with an inlaid baseball diamond floor and replica scoreboard over the bar. The nightly rate was $2,500 ($15,900), immortalized by the *Guinness Book of World Records* as "the world's costliest hotel accommodation."[222]

Elvis Presley checked into the Celestial Suite on several occasions, and became friendly with the Judge. The Celestial Suite, as well as the Judge's quarters in the Astrodome, were not unlike Presley's Graceland, and as *Houston Chronicle* columnist Lisa Gray noted years later, it's not too hard to see the link between Hofheinz and Elvis—both born showmen but also poor Southern kids who craved luxury.[*]

Shortly afterwards, Hofheinz obtained state approval to open a new bank, and the Astro Bank was opened for business in the stadium complex, with the Judge installed as president and CEO.

[*]Lisa Gray "Dene Hofheinz looks back at Houston, family history" *Houston Chronicle* July 1, 2007

In the span of a single decade, Hofheinz had transformed a humid, empty prairie into a vast entertainment complex centered on one of the world's most innovative buildings. He called it all The Astrodomain. The empire sat on 500 acres of land that was either owned by Hofheinz, or controlled by him through county leases. As the decade drew to a close, over 100 of those acres remained unimproved, and Hofheinz continued to think big: "As long as I am alive, or my son behind me, I don't think we will ever complete the Dome or quit making improvements. When we do, that is the day somebody else will be patting us in the face with a spade."[223]

The 1970s, however, would prove much less kind.

In May 1970, just a few months into the new decade, Hofheinz suffered a crippling stroke. He survived the stroke, but its long-term effects were devastating. The Grand Huckster, who had strode confidently and spoken so eloquently, would spend most of his remaining life confined to a wheelchair, with his speech frequently impaired. The prodigious meals he had once enjoyed gave way to doctors' orders as he was placed on a strict diet, which he attempted to break at every opportunity. Although his mind remained sharp, the overall decline in the Judge's health affected his ability to run the business; Tal Smith recalled that during this period Hofheinz "was not the same man that he had been during the earlier years."[224]

As the Judge's health faltered, the business climate presented even greater challenges. In the first decade of the franchise's existence, the Colt .45s and Astros had posted nine losing seasons (with the tenth closing out at exactly .500). In the years after the Judge gained control of the Astros, baseball income was diverted to other ventures, and there was much criticism of the team's management as a parade of promising young players were traded away.[225] The Astros' annual attendance at the Dome during this period had its ups and downs, but the overall trend was down.

The Astrodomain struggled on other fronts as well. The amusement park made money, but was falling short of expectations in terms of profitability. Mired in red ink after only four years of operation, the Astro Bank was closed by state regulators in 1975, and an FDIC suit lingered for years.

Nine stories above, in the Astroworld Hotel's Celestial Suite, Hofheinz kept up opulent appearances. He and his wife had more or less moved into the lavish suite, and now spent most of their nights there. They were, however, quick to yield to paying guests: behind the scenes, the Judge was scrambling for cash to keep the Astrodomain above water.

The Judge had always been heavily leveraged, and, once separated from Bob Smith's deep pockets, had been forced to rely on a patchwork of bank financing. The latest burst of Astrodomain construction— in particular, the hotel penthouse—left the organization heavily in debt. Moreover, many of his loans were tied to the prime interest rate, which began to skyrocket starting in 1972. By the middle of the decade, he had consolidated his debts into a single $38 million ($165 million) package, but the interest rate on that loan floated at four percent above prime, with payments due every ninety days. It was a crushing burden, and income from baseball and the other Astro-domain interests were simply not able to keep up. As the Astrodome's tenth anniversary approached, an interviewer asked Hofheinz: "Have you ever stopped being a showman?" After a pause, Hofheinz replied, "I can't afford to."[226]

Hofheinz faced increasing pressure from his creditors, who began to clamor for sale of assets. The Judge had clung tenaciously to his acquisitions throughout his business career, and was unwilling to part with his prize possessions, whether a hotel, an antique carousel, or his private railroad car.

Unmoved, the creditors joined forces, organizing a new three-man board of directors and seizing control from the Hofheinz family in June 1975. Hofheinz remained the Astrodomain's chairman of the board, but in reality he had been kicked upstairs. The creditors were now in control of operations, and empowered to shed properties to raise cash. One by one, the pieces of the empire slipped away. As-troworld had previously been leased to Six Flags, and the four hotels were sold by early 1976.

The cash raised by these transactions reduced the debt, but not enough. Finally, in September 1976, the Judge was forced out. The Hofheinz family sold the baseball team and the remnants of the As-trodomain to the creditors. In an episode reminiscent of the short-fuse

Bob Smith buyout in 1965, Hofheinz was given a one-week option period to raise cash to repurchase the team.

But this time there would be no miraculous comeback. The option expired in October 1976, and Hofheinz's ties to the HSA and the Astros were completely severed.

It was over. Hofheinz moved out of the Dome for good. It took forty-eight moving vans to remove his personal furnishings and vast antiques collection out of the Dome and to a warehouse.˙ The lavish Astrodome apartment and the Celestial Suite were left behind as Hofheinz and his wife moved to a large but conventional home in River Oaks.

After completing the move and settling into his new home, Hofheinz and his wife made plans to lease a Skybox for the Astros' 1977 season, but word came back that the new management preferred he stay away from the Astrodome. They believed that the Judge's presence in the building he had once commanded would be too disruptive to employees as they transitioned to a new organization. That season, he stayed home and watched games on television. In the years following he was seldom seen in the Astrodome.[227]

In his later years, Hofheinz changed his personal style. Reflecting the tastes of the 1970s, he traded his trademark black suits for loud sports coats, and began wearing a necklace. Because his paralysis made it difficult for him to shave, he grew a large beard. More than one observer noted a striking resemblance to Orson Welles.

Hofheinz died of a heart attack in his River Oaks home in 1982 at the age of 70.

Years earlier, he had told a friend that when he died he wanted to be brought to the Astrodome for one night, with his "toes pointed straight up at the top of the dome."[228] This intriguing notion, conjuring images of a papal funeral beneath the great dome of St. Peter's Basilica, did not come to pass—his funeral was held in a church. But after the services, his hearse and accompanying motorcade made a detour to South Main Street.

There, the funeral procession slowly circled the Astrodome, where the flags flew at half-staff, and every employee came outside and lined the curb to bid farewell to the Grand Huckster.

---

˙Many of these belongings were auctioned off in an epic 7-day estate sale in 1984.

# BEYOND THE ASTRODOME

# CHAPTER TWENTY-THREE

# THE LAST GAME

ON OCTOBER 9, 1999, the Atlanta Braves were playing the Astros in the Dome in the fourth game of the National League Divisional Series. The Astros were on the brink of elimination in the five-game series, which the Braves led two games to one. Game Four was turning out to be a rollercoaster: after six innings the Braves led 7–0, but in the seventh and eighth the Astros had fought back with five runs.

Now the Astros were batting in the bottom of the ninth with two outs and a man on second. Third baseman Ken Caminiti, representing the tying run, was at the plate. Caminiti had hit a three-run homer in the previous inning and was a very serious offensive threat.

Atlanta reliever John Rocker wound up and delivered a breaking ball that Caminiti hit solidly to center. Rocker spun around and watched in horror as the ball soared deeper and deeper into the outfield, but his teammate Andrew Jones trotted easily back to catch it.[229] Rocker was fortunate: the Dome had remained a pitcher's park up until the very end. Atlanta won the game 7–5, and with it the series. The Braves jubilantly trotted off the field, and went on to the National League Championship series, and eventually the World Series.

The Astros cleared out their lockers and went home. This small drama ended their 1999 season, and with it professional sports in the Astrodome.

The years following Hofheinz's death had not been kind to the Dome. In 1987, with Bud Adams and the Oilers complaining about lack of seating, and threatening a move to Jacksonville, the stadium underwent a $50 million renovation. The project had added 15,000 seats, but swept away the great two-acre scoreboard and Hofheinz's right-field suite, which had been unoccupied for years. The renovations had mollified Adams, but only temporarily—just ten years later in 1997, the Oilers departed for Nashville, where a new, football-only stadium awaited them.

Judge Hofheinz had once told a reporter, "Unless they invent a miracle drug I don't know anything about, I won't be around to make the last payment in fifty years."[230] His prophecy proved correct, but not only Hofheinz was gone. Now the Astros were leaving too—they would begin their 2000 season at brand-new Enron Field in downtown Houston. The Astrodome itself was nudged aside as a sports venue a mere thirty-five years after it opened, and the final payment had not yet been made.

Structurally, the Dome was sound, but commercially, it had become obsolete. For all the Astro-hype, the building did not make it to the twenty-first century as a major league venue.

A generation earlier, the press had lauded the Astrodome and its multipurpose cousins in New York, Philadelphia, Cincinnati, and St Louis. Reporters were awed by the new stadiums, advocated for domes in their cities, and confidently anticipated artificial turf in every venue. But tastes were changing, and the press was turning its back. Like nearly all of the stadiums built in the 1960s, the Dome had become an object of ridicule in the press: a week before the final game, a *Seattle Times* headline sneered: STERILE ASTRODOME A NECESSARY EVIL IN HUMID HOUSTON, and the accompanying story opined, "Undoubtedly, the Astrodome will be one of baseball's least-missed facilities."[231]

The Astros' new home at Enron Field, named for the doomed Houston-based energy giant,* represented baseball's new generation of facilities, and in many ways stood as a rejection of its predecessor. Rather than a suburban site, the new stadium was situated in the heart of downtown Houston, adjacent to Union Station. Originally constructed in 1911, the station had been abandoned as a rail terminal since 1974.[232] Now, the old building had been renovated and skillfully integrated into the new stadium complex.

---

* In the wake of Enron's ignominious collapse in 2001, the new stadium was renamed Minute Maid Park.

The ballpark itself eschewed any visual association with the twenty-first century; instead it incorporated comforting traditional forms, compatible with the adjacent rail terminal but more importantly evoking the *ersatz* beer-and-pretzels look that was becoming fashionable at new stadiums. The playing field and surrounding seating were deliberately asymmetrical, with nooks and crannies that intentionally recalled early-twentieth-century ballparks. Visually, Enron Field looked more like Ebbets Field than it did the Astrodome. It was in many ways a repeat of the wave of new stadiums built in the era of Woodrow Wilson—and the structures themselves deliberately mimicked that era.

And this was a baseball-only venue, matching another nationwide trend: the 1960s multipurpose stadiums were being demolished or abandoned across the land. Football would be played elsewhere.

But while the new stadium deliberately turned its back on the Astrodome's character, it also demonstrated the Dome's relentless influence. Yes, there was an old-timey, hand-operated scoreboard, but it was hedged with plenty of modern electronics. The giant diamond vision display in center field was a direct descendent of the Dome's huge scoreboard, and it pushed the media envelope even further. The new display served not merely as a reminder of television, it frequently *was* a television, playing local weather reports and other programming directly from local TV stations. In a small hat-tip to the Astrodome, the giant display occasionally played the original low-resolution Astrodome animations, eliciting smiles and applause, mostly from fans of a certain age.

Of course, the new stadium had luxury boxes. Hofheinz's spur-of-the-moment innovation had become an economic cornerstone of the industry. And it went without saying that there would be air conditioning; Houston's climate remained as challenging as ever. Smoking, however, was forbidden. If you wanted to light up, you were consigned to designated open-air areas on the perimeter of the stadium.*

Then there was the grass.

At its high-water mark in the late 1980s, artificial turf was the playing surface in ten major league ballparks, and nearly 40 percent

---

* Smoking had been banned in the Astrodome, and other such venues in Houston, in 1992.

of major-league games were played on it. Now that market share was rapidly dwindling. Artificial turf was being blamed for an increase in player injuries. But perhaps more important, it did not fit into the nostalgia that baseball was now embracing in its new ballparks. "Baseball was meant to be played outdoors," Astros owner Drayton McLane Jr. said. "And it was meant to be played on natural grass."[233] Houston, the birthplace of AstroTurf, was very much a part of the back-to-nature trend: the new park had natural grass.

Perhaps the most ironic difference: a retractable roof that could be opened to the sky. After thirty-six years, outdoor baseball would return to Houston—but only on days when outside temperatures were reasonably cool—and the grass would have unfettered access to sunlight on a regular basis.

At the time the new ballpark opened in 2000, the Astros management was learning how to operate their new stadium, and experimenting with the tradeoffs that came with a retractable roof: opening it between games would admit sunlight for the grass, but keeping it closed would keep the interior cooler. The question became: how long could the roof remain closed without jeopardizing the grass?

The new stadium's groundskeeper told the Associated Press, "If we had to close [the roof] for six or seven days I'd have to wait and see. We'd like to be able to open it to get some sun every day." He frankly admitted, "We don't know for sure, this is all new for us."[234]

True enough the roof was new, but the question had come up before. It was much like the dilemma that had faced the men who had gathered in a college classroom forty years earlier and just a few miles away, scrawling formulas on a chalkboard and wondering how they might get grass to grow in the biggest room in the world.

# ACKNOWLEDGMENTS

Many people have made enormous contributions to the research and production of this book.

Thanks to everyone who agreed to meet with me for interviews, and for sharing their memories and insights: Dene Hofheinz Anton, Barbara Smith Armstrong, former Mayor Fred Hofheinz, I.A. Naman, Joe Siff, Tal Smith, Barry Moore, and Dr. King Odell.

Barry Moore and Anna Mod read the manuscript and provided many insightful suggestions and corrections. Any remaining factual errors are mine, not theirs.

Everyone that I met during my frequent visits to the Houston Public Library, and the Houston Metropolitan Research Center was very courteous and helpful. Timothy J. Ronk and Joel Draut deserve special mention for the hours they spent poring over HMRC's extensive collection of negatives in search of period photographs of the Astrodome. I am very grateful for their time, patience, and diligence. Vince Lee and Greg Yerke were very helpful in navigating the University of Houston Libraries Special Collections. Thanks also to Sarah Jackson, who pointed me to some very helpful resources in the Harris County Archives, and to Rebecca Russell and Melissa Kean at Rice University's Woodson Research Center.

Tom Darling kindly gave me permission to publish his iconic photo of the Astrodome groundbreaking. Michael McCorkle allowed me to include construction-period site photographs taken by Peter Whitney. You can find more photos by Whitney in Michael's book *Life and Times Around Bellaire, Texas*, available at www.bellairebook.com.

Brent Shyer, Vice President of Special Projects for O'Malley Seidler Partners, secured permission for me to quote from Walter O'Malley's letters, and also pointed me to his impressive research on O'Malley's domed stadium project.

Mark Miller patiently endured my frequent telephone calls and arranged for me to visit the Astrodome, which is now closed to the public. Barbara McKnight gave me a tour of the former Smith-Hofheinz headquarters on Brandt Street that she now operates as Hofheinz House.

Thanks also go to Greg Allen, Carrie Cantor, Steve Grande, Doug Kirk, Barbara Morales, Paul Rapp, Nancy Gast Romps, George Smalley, and Mike Vance.

# SOURCES

The facts presented in this book are drawn from a wide array of materials, and my research focused on primary sources.

## ARCHIVAL COLLECTIONS

Thankfully, many important records regarding the Astrodome have been carefully preserved in various archival collections.

The most important of these is the Robert J. Minchew Houston Astrodome Architectural and Engineering Collection, at the Dolph Briscoe Center for American History, University of Texas at Austin. Minchew was the Associated Architects' on-site representative during design and construction of the Astrodome, and his involvement continued with various follow-on projects for ten years after. Minchew, it seems, saved nearly everything that came across his desk during this period. The collection is remarkably comprehensive, and it became the technical backbone of the story told in this book.

George Kirksey's papers are preserved at the University of Houston Libraries Special Collections. They provide a good overview of Kirksey's history with the Colt .45s and Astros.

Rice University's Woodson Research Center holds the papers of Astrodome architects and Rice alumni Ralph Anderson (MS413) and Arthur Jones (MS535).

The Harris County Archives hold the papers of County Judge William M. Elliott (CR031) and County Commissioner E.A. "Squatty" Lyons (MC001). Elliott presided over the county commissioners' court during design and construction of the Astrodome, and the collection provides correspondence, contracts, and photographs documenting the project. Lyons' papers include a remarkable collection of scrapbooks compiled by his staff. The enormous scrapbooks contain thousands of newspaper clippings and other mementos. The volumes covering the early 1960s are dominated by coverage of the Domed Stadium, providing an invaluable chronicle of the project.

The Houston Public Library's Houston Metropolitan Research Center (HMRC) maintains large files on Hofheinz and the Astrodome, as well as the many related topics recounted in this book. I drew heavily on the following HMRC collections: Democratic National Convention, 1928, Records (MSS0056); Frank J. Schlueter/ Bank of the Southwest Collection (MSS0100); Litterst-Dixon Photograph Collection (MSS1248); Evelyn Norton Anderson Papers (MSS 1465); Houston Press Collection (RGD0005); and the *Houston Post* Photographic Collection (RGD0006). The papers of Judge Hofheinz (MSS 1036) were being processed in late 2013, and I had an opportunity to view three Astrodome scrapbooks that will be included in this collection.

Barry Moore provided a small collection of materials he gathered while conducting research for a 1995 symposium on the Astrodome. This collection included interviews (described below), movies, and articles. These materials have since been donated to the Houston Metropolitan Research Center.

## INTERVIEWS

Several persons generously shared their recollections of the Astrodome's early days, as well as related subjects. Two of the Judge's children, Dene Hofheinz Anton and former Mayor Fred Hofheinz, met with me and shared their memories during lengthy interviews. Both were understandably proud of their father's achievements, yet very candid about his faults. I.A. Naman told me about his distinguished engineering career, and the unprecedented challenges he faced while designing the Dome's air-conditioning system. Tal Smith shared his experiences as an aide to Judge Hofheinz, as well as his subsequent and very successful career as a senior executive with the Astros as well as the New York Yankees. Joe Siff and Barbara Smith Armstrong provided many valuable stories about the Judge and the early days of the Astrodome. Barry Moore knew all of the Astrodome architects and engineers, and he provided very helpful recollections and perspectives about S.I. Morris, Hermon Lloyd, Ralph Anderson, and Talbott Wilson. Barry also shared transcripts of his unpublished interviews with S.I. Morris, Al Jensen, Ken Zimmerman, and I.A. Naman. Dr. King Odell told me about the debut of artificial turf at the Moses Brown School. I also took advantage of HMRC oral histories, including Larry Dierker, Mickey Herskowitz, and Fred Hofheinz.

## PERIODICALS

I drew heavily on contemporaneous articles and photos in the *Houston Chronicle*, and the now-defunct *Houston Post*, both of which are available on microfilm at the Houston Public Library. Many of these articles are also found in the archival collections listed above. *Sports Illustrated* generously maintains a superb archive of articles online at http://sportsillustrated.cnn.com/vault/.

## ONLINE RESOURCES

The Handbook of Texas Online (http://www.tshaonline.org/handbook/), published by the Texas State Historical Association, was an invaluable resource for a wide range of topics. O'Malley Seidler Partners maintains www.walteromalley.com, a website tribute to Walter O'Malley that includes an online archive of O'Malley's correspondence about the Brooklyn domed stadium project. This collection is fascinating, although a few of the documents are heavily redacted.

## EPHEMERA

The Houston Sports Association published a wide variety of publicity materials, starting in 1965 with the 260-page souvenir book *Inside the Astrodome*, which is one of the most comprehensive collections of technical data about the building. A subsequent publication, *Astrodomain*, published in 1972, includes descriptions of the completed hotel and entertainment complex. HSA also published postcards depicting not just the building but also the events within, such as the Boy Scout Circus, and boat show described in the text.

## SELECTED BIBLIOGRAPHY

Leonardo Benevolo, *History of Modern Architecture*, Volume 1. Cambridge: MIT Press, 1977.

Cole, Thomas. *No Color Is My Kind: The Life of Eldrewey Stearns and the Integration of Houston*. Austin: University of Texas Press, 2012. Kindle edition.

Federal Writers' Project. *Houston, a History and Guide*. Houston: Anson Jones Press, 2012. Kindle edition.

Forrestal, Dan. *Faith, Hope & $5,000: The Story of Monsanto*. New York: Simon & Schuster, 1977.

Gershman, Michael. *Diamonds: The Evolution of the Ballpark from Elysian Fields to Camden Yards*. Boston: Houghton Mifflin, 1993.

Giles, Bill with Doug Myers. *Pouring Six Beers at a Time*. Chicago: Triumph Books, 2007. Kindle edition.

Historic American Engineering Record (Library of Congress). *Houston Astrodome, 8400 Kirby Drive, Houston, Harris County, TX.*, HAER TX-108. http://www.loc.gov/pictures/item/tx1045/, accessed December 8, 2013.

King, Ross. *Brunelleschi's Dome*. New York: Penguin, 2000.

Mark, Robert (ed.). *Architectural Technology up to the Scientific Revolution: the Art and Structure of Large-scale Buildings*. Cambridge: MIT Press, 1995.

McComb, David G. *Houston: A History*. Austin: University of Texas Press, 1981.

Mod, Anna. *Building Modern Houston*. Charleston: Arcadia Publishing, 2011.

Moore, Barry. "Building a Houston Practice – The Career of S.I. Morris." *Cite: The Architecture + Design Review of Houston*, No. 43, Winter 1999.

Moore, Barry. "The Morris Effect." *Cite: The Architecture + Design Review of Houston*, No. 68, Fall 2006.

Nealon, Clark, Robert Nottebart, Stanley Siegel, & James Tinsley. "The Campaign for Major League Baseball in Houston." *The Houston Review*, Vol. 7, No 1, 1985. A Houston sportswriter collaborated with three historians to create this carefully researched and documented chronicle of the efforts to establish a major league baseball team in Houston.

Ray, Edgar W. *The Grand Huckster*. Memphis: Memphis State University Press, 1980. *Huckster* is the biography of Judge Roy Hofheinz, published in 1980, just two years before the Judge died. Ray was a friend of the Judge and his book is overwhelmingly favorable, but it provides very comprehensive reporting on Hofheinz's life and the creation of the Astrodome. Ray was able to interview many of the persons who played key roles in the project, and their quotes, although sometimes guarded, bring great life to the story.

Reed, Robert. *A Six-Gun Salute: An Illustrated History of the Colt .45s*. Houston: Lone Star Books, 1999.

Shapiro, Michael. *Bottom of the Ninth: Branch Rickey, Casey Stengel, and the Daring Scheme to Save Baseball from Itself*. Henry Holt and Co., 2010. Kindle edition.

Shapiro, Michael. *The Last Good Season: Brooklyn, The Dodgers, and their Final Pennant Race Together*. New York: Broadway Books, 2003.

Stamper, John W. "The Galerie des Machines of the 1889 Paris World's Fair." *Technology and Culture*, Vol. 30, No. 2, April 1989.

Stein, Benjamin. *Building Technology: Mechanical and Electrical Systems*. New York: John Wiley & Sons, 1997.

Strom, Steven. *Houston Lost and Unbuilt*. Austin: University of Texas Press, 2010.

Titchener, Campbell B. *The George Kirksey Story*. Austin: Eakin Press, 1989.

Trumpbour. Robert C. *The New Cathedrals: Politics and Media in the History of Stadium Construction*. Syracuse University Press, Kindle Edition, 2007.

Vance, Mike. *Houston's Sporting Life 1900-1950*. Charleston: Arcadia Publishing, 2011.

Wilkinson, Chris. *Supersheds: The Architecture of Long-span, Large-volume Buildings*. Butterworth Architecture, 1991.

# ENDNOTES

1  Details of Chicago presentation and Lou Perini quote: Dick Peebles, "Cullinan Gives Houston's Plans for Debut in N.L.," *Houston Chronicle*, October 18, 1960.
2  "Hofheinz Impressed Stengel," *Houston Chronicle*, April 8, 1965.
3  Tal Smith, interview with the author, Sugar Land, Texas, May 17, 2013.
4  Lothar Bucher, quoted in Leonardo Benevolo, *History of Modern Architecture, Vol. 1: The Tradition of Modern Architecture, Volume 1* (Cambridge, MA: MIT Press, 1977).
5  British Museum, "The Great Exhibition," http://www.bl.uk/learning/histcitizen/victorians/exhibition/greatexhibition.html, accessed January 13, 2014.
6  John W. Stamper, "The Galerie des Machines of the 1889 Paris World's Fair," *Technology and Culture*, Volume 30, No. 2 (April 1989), 330-353.
7  Stamper, "The Galerie des Machines," 330-353.
8  George Gipe, "An Indoor Football Game Was One of the Sport's Darkest," *Sports Illustrated*, December 5, 1977.
9  "New Ebbets Field to Have Hot Dogs and Hot Seats," *New York Times*, March 6, 1952.
10 Letter from Walter O'Malley to Buckminster Fuller, May 26, 1955, http://www.walteromalley.com/docu_detail.php?gallery=1&set=18&docuID=185&pageNum=1, accessed March 31, 2013. Reprinted by permission.
11 "Dodger Head Hails Studies Made for Domed Stadium," *New York Times*, November 23, 1955.
12 Letter from Robert Moses to Walter O'Malley, November 2, 1953, http://www.walteromalley.com/docu_gallery.php?gallery=1&set=2, accessed November 19, 2013. Reprinted by permission.
13 Houston of the early 1950s: Federal Writers' Project, *Houston, a History and Guide* [Kindle Edition]; Thomas Martin, "Mayor Gave Self Big Job: Here's Result," *Houston Press*, July 1, 1953; and "Here's What Mayor Hofheinz Plans for Houston," *Houston Press*, January 2, 1953.
14 McCarthy enclosed stadium proposal: Clyde La Motte, "McCarthy Bares Stadium Plan, Waits Action on Pro Franchise," *Houston Post*, January 20, 1950; "Stadium Plan Alive Yet, Says McCarthy," *Houston Post*, January 21, 1950.
15 "Baseball Executive Tells Houston Story," *Houston Post*, January 29, 1961.
16 1957 state legislation: Campbell B. Titchener, *The George Kirksey Story* (Austin: Eakin Press, 1989), 77-78; Clark Nealon, Robert Nottebart, Stanley Siegel, & James Tinsley, "The Campaign for Major League Baseball in Houston," *The Houston Review*, Vol. 7, No. 5 (1985).
17 Cost figures were escalated to year 2013 using the U.S. Bureau of Labor Statistics CPI Inflation Calculator: http://www.bls.gov/data/inflation_calculator.htm.
18 Dick Peebles, "Stadium Group Mulls Over Unique Plans," *Houston Chronicle*, May 8, 1958.
19 Nealon et. al., "Campaign for Baseball," 23.

20  S.I. Morris, interview by Barry Moore, ca 1994.
21  Dene Hofheinz Anton, interview by the author. Houston, February 9, 2014.
22  Edgar W. Ray, *The Grand Huckster* (Memphis: Memphis State University Press, 1980), 245, 248, Appendix A.
23  Fred Hofheinz, interview by the author. Houston, August 30, 2013.
24  Ibid.
25  Dance promotions and Model T "breakdown": Ray, *The Grand Huckster*, 17-18, and Ernest Bailey, "Like a Carnival, Usher Recalls," *Houston Post*, undated article in 1928 Convention vertical file, HMRC.
26  Ancestry.com. "1930 United States Federal Census [database online]." Original data: United States of America, Bureau of the Census. Fifteenth Census of the United States, 1930. Washington, D.C.: National Archives and Records Administration, 1930.
27  Hofheinz and Johnson at 1928 convention: Ray, *The Grand Huckster*, 21-22.
28  Ray, *The Grand Huckster*, Appendix A.
29  LBJ 1941 and 1948 senate campaigns: Ray, *The Grand Huckster*, 106, 166. At the time the Astrodome opened, many contemporary accounts described Hofheinz as "LBJ's campaign manager," incorrectly implying that Hofheinz had run the statewide campaigns.
30  Sam Houston Hall details: National Lumber Manufacturers Association, "The Lamella Roof," *Lumber and Its Utilization* (1928); "Formal Opening of Hall Today," *New York Times*, June 24, 1928; Steven Strom, *Houston Lost and Unbuilt* (Austin: University of Texas Press, 2010), 12-13.
31  Promised he would make money: Ray, *The Grand Huckster*, 132-133
32  Bumping *I Love Lucy*: "Roy Hofheinz, Ex-judge, Mayor, Dies," *Houston Post*, November 22, 1982; Gary Cartwright, "A Barnum Named Hofheinz, A Big Top Called Astrodome," *New York Times*, July 21, 1968.
33  Fred Hofheinz, interview by the author, Houston, August 30, 2013.
34  Dene Hofheinz Anton, interview by the author, Houston, February 9, 2014.
35  S.I. Morris, interview by Sandra Curtis Levy conducted for the Archives of American Art, Texas Project Oral History Transcripts, Archives of American Art, Smithsonian Institution. [Microfilm reel no. 3752], March 20, 1981.
36  Ray, *The Grand Huckster*, 189.
37  "Southwest Development Will Include 120 Stores," *Houston Chronicle*, February 9, 1958.
38  Ray, *The Grand Huckster*, 257.
39  Fred Hofheinz, interview by the author, Houston, August 30, 2013.
40  Nealon et. al., "Campaign for Baseball," 25.
41  Barry Moore, "Building A Houston Practice," *Cite: The Architecture + Design Review of Houston*, No. 043, Winter 1999.
42  *The Greening of the Astrodome: An Experience in Collaboration* (unfinished manuscript, ca.1972), Robert J. Minchew Houston Astrodome Architectural and Engineering Collection, 1928-1990, Dolph Briscoe Center for American History, The University of Texas at Austin. Box 94-274-18. Minchew's papers include multiple drafts of the first chapter of this manuscript, which is unsigned and undated. Various references in the text point to Talbott Wilson as the author, writing sometime around 1972. An outline included with the manuscript indicates that the author intended to cover the same topic and focus on the same time period as this book.
43  *Greening of the Astrodome*.

44  Brandt Street office furnishings and decoration: Roy Terrell, "Fast Man with a .45", *Sports Illustrated*, March 26, 1962.

45  The account of the 1960 Brandt Street meeting is drawn from Ray, *The Grand Huckster*, 304; Rosanna Ruiz, "Seth Irvin Morris, Whose Architectural Firm Designed the Astrodome, Dies," *Houston Chronicle*, August 2, 2006; and "The Campaign for Baseball in Houston," *The Houston Review*, Vol. 7, No. 1 (1985), 36-37.

46  Clark Nealon, "All-Weather Sports Stadium Planned for Site Off South Main," *Houston Post*, August 21, 1960; "Houston to Build Stadium Covered by Translucent Dome," *New York Times*, August 21, 1960.

47  "U.S. Mayors in Naples," *New York Times*, September 18, 1955.

48  Ray, *The Grand Huckster*, Appendix A.

49  Cullinan and Kirksey statements about schedule: "Houston Expecting No Trouble In Building Park, Buying Buffs," Associated Press story in *New York Times*, October 18, 1960; "National League Gets New York Bid," UPI story in *New York Times*, October 11, 1960.

50  Thomas R. Cole, *No Color Is My Kind: The Life of Eldrewey Stearns and the Integration of Houston* (Austin: University of Texas Press, Kindle edition, 2012), Kindle locations 1399-1401.

51  Fred Hofheinz, interview by the author, Houston, August 30, 2013.

52  Harold Scarlett, "Bonds for Stadium Win in Record Vote," *Houston Post*, February 1, 1961.

53  Vernon Fewell, "Sports Stadium to Combine Old With New Ideas," *Houston Chronicle*, February 5, 1961.

54  An interview of S.I. Morris conducted Mar. 20, 1981, by Sandra Curtis Levy, for the Archives of American Art. Texas Project Oral History Transcripts, Archives of American Art, Smithsonian Institution. [Microfilm reel 3752].

55  An interview of S.I. Morris conducted Mar. 20, 1981, by Sandra Curtis Levy, for the Archives of American Art. Texas Project Oral History Transcripts, Archives of American Art, Smithsonian Institution [Microfilm reel 3752].

56  S.I. Morris, interview by Barry Moore, ca. 1994.

57  Clark Nealon, "All-Weather Sports Stadium Planned for Site off South Main," *Houston Post*, August 21, 1960; James W. Fitzgibbon, Synergetics letter to Ralph Anderson, June 16, 1961; Minchew, 94-274-01.

58  Elon E. Ellis, Vice President Timber Structures, Inc., letter to S.I. Morris, January 6, 1961; Minchew, 94-274-01.

59  "Lamella Roof Construction," undated, published by Lamella Roof Associates, St. Louis, Missouri; Minchew, 94-274-18.

60  Robert Minchew, Letter to Mr. Edwin M. Long, April 29, 1964; Minchew, 94-274-10.

61  Royal Albert Hall: "The Building," http://www.royalalberthall.com/uploaded-Files/About_The_Hall/assets/History_of_the_Royal_Albert_Hall.pdf, accessed July 21, 2013.

62  Memorandum Conference at WMCA, February 2, 1961; Minchew, 94-274-10.

63  Robert B. Newman letter to Talbott Wilson, March 14, 1961; Memorandum Conference at WMCA, February 2, 1961; Minchew, 94-274-10.

64  Skylight pattern on roof: Talbott Wilson, "Acoustic-Architectural Considerations in the Harris County Domed Stadium," presented October 13, 1965, at the Seventeenth Annual Fall Convention of the Audio Engineering Society, New York; Minchew, 94-274-18; Robert Minchew, letter to Mr. Edwin M. Long, April 29, 1964; Minchew, 94-274-10.

65  Full-scale simulation at Hitchcock: memoranda from Ralph Anderson to stadium architects and Judge Hofheinz, August 4, 1961, and September 25, 1961.

66  diffusing layer added to avoid glare: "Dynamic Houston: The Domed Stadium," Chamber of Commerce notes in Minchew, 94-274-18; and *Inside the Astrodome*, 30.

67  John Wilson, "Fabulous Dome Gets Dress Rehearsal," *Houston Chronicle*, February 9, 1965.

68  George Kirksey, letter to S.I. Morris, September 5, 1958; Minchew, 94-274-8.

69  "Smoking and Health: Report of the Advisory Committee to the Surgeon General of the Public Health Service" (1964), http://profiles.nlm.nih.gov/ps/access/NNBBMQ.ocr, accessed July 4, 2013.

70  Ralph Anderson biography: Rice University Fondren Library, "Guide to Ralph Anderson Jr. Papers," https://library.rice.edu/collections/WRC/finding-aids/manuscripts/0413 - ref7, accessed October 25, 2013.

71  The Judge Takes on the Colosseum for the Covered-Arena Championship," *National Observer*, April 19, 1965.

72  Tal Smith, interview by the author, Sugar Land, Texas, May 17, 2013.

73  Ralph Anderson, letter to R.I. Peters of Bigelow-Sanford Carpet Company, Inc., April 7, 1961, Minchew, 94-274-10. Anderson's confidence may have resulted from his collaboration with Phillips, the physicist.

74  G.C. Phillips, "Preliminary Report to Wilson, Morris, Crain, and Anderson, Architects on the Harris County Sports Stadium by G.C. Phillips, Consulting Physicist," January 2, 1961; Minchew, 94-274-10.

75  Ray, *The Grand Huckster*, 304.

76  Suggestions for dynamic systems mounted within the roof: Memorandum of Lunch Meeting May 1, 1962, and Memorandum of Conference at Rice Institute, 15 December 1960; Minchew, 94-274-10.

77  R.C. Potts letter to Ralph Anderson, January 17, 1962; Minchew, 94-274-11.

78  William O. Trogdon, letters to Ralph Anderson dated July 12, 1961, and January 13, 1962; and "Selection of Turfgrass or Turfgrasses for Use in Harris County Sports Stadium," dated July 12, 1961; Minchew, 94-274-11.

79  Ralph Anderson, letter to Mr. O.J. Noer, September 18, 1961; Minchew, 94-274-11.

80  A&M study findings: Ethan C. Holt, Texas A&M University College of Agriculture, letter to Ralph Anderson, January 15, 1964; "The Growth of Grass (turf) with Limited Light," Research Report, Texas A&M University, Texas Agricultural Experiment Station, Soil and Crop Sciences Department, College Station, Texas, 1963; Minchew, 94-274-10.

81  Ray, *The Grand Huckster*, 306-7; Roger Davis of 3M, letter to Si Morris, March 12, 1964; Minchew, 94-274-10.

82  Ralph Dodd, "Stadium Wood Floor Studied for Meets," *Houston Post*, June 14, 1964.

83  "Shelters in Big Cities Sought By Kennedy," *New York Times*, July 27, 1961.

84  "Domed Stadium Studied as Atom Fallout Shelter," *Houston Chronicle*, August 4, 1961.

85  Thomas Martin, "Raps U.S. for Hiding Truth From People," *Houston Press*, December 15, 1953.

86  Lyndon Baines Johnson Presidential Library, "Daily Diary Collection," http://www.lbjlibrary.net/collections/daily-diary.html, accessed July 2, 2013.

87  Tom Omstead, "Fallout Shelter in Arena Could Hold 150,000," *Houston Chronicle*, August 13, 1961.

88   Ed Ray, "How 38,000 Would be Protected from Atomic Fallout in Stadium,"
     *Houston Press*, September 1, 1961.
89   Federal grant to Harris County: draft of contract between Department of Defense
     and Harris County Texas, Harris County Judge William M. Elliott Papers CR031
     1956-1976, Harris County Archives, Box 1446, Folder 39; Ralph A. Anderson,
     letter to Judge Bill Elliott. August 28, 1961; Minchew, 94-274-11.
90   Ray, *The Grand Huckster*, 272-273.
91   *The Greening of the Astrodome.*
92   George Kirksey letter to Si Morris, September 5, 1958.
93   Site planning criteria: *The Greening of the Astrodome* and "Preliminary
     Architectural Program and Site Area Considerations for a Sport Center for
     Harris County" 1958; Minchew, 94-274-1.
94   *The Greening of the Astrodome*
95   Cole, *No Color*, Kindle location 1425.
96   James M. Markham, "A Lot Better Than A War," *New York Times*,
     February 8, 1987.
97   "Houston-Harris County Fallout Shelter Project," Elliott, 1446-31.
98   Barry Moore, "Building a Houston Practice – The Career of S.I. Morris," *Cite:
     The Architecture + Design Review of Houston*, No. 43, Winter 1999, 30.
99   Statement to the Harris County Commissioners Court from The Associated
     Stadium Architects, May 28, 1962; Minchew, 94-274-01.
100  Sigman Byrd, "Dry Pit Could Be Dandy Lake," *Houston Chronicle*,
     July 24, 1962.
101  Statement to the Harris County Commissioners Court from The Associated
     Stadium Architects, May 28, 1962; Minchew, 94-274-01.
102  Astrodome Construction Documents 1963–64, Arthur E. Jones Architectural
     Records, MS 535, Woodson Research Center, Fondren Library, Rice University,
     Box 16.
103  Cost plus a dollar: Al Jensen, interview by Barry Moore, ca.1994.
104  Al Jensen background and 1962 construction bids: Ernest Bailey, "Stadium: $19.4
     Million, County Needs $6.6 Million to Build It," *Houston Press*, November 29, 1962;
     John Ira Petty, "Those folks Who Built the Incredible Dome," *Houston Post*, April
     9, 1990; Al Jensen, interview by Barry Moore, 1994; Melanie Markley, "Al Jensen,
     Executive of Firm that Built Dome," *Houston Chronicle*, February 18, 2004.
105  Sound trucks in African-American neighborhoods: Bill Giles with Doug Myers.
     *Pouring Six Beers at a Time.* (Chicago: Triumph Books, Kindle Edition), 60;
     "Judge Roy Builds His Own Monument," *National Observer*, April 29, 1968.
106  "Domed Stadium Starts Going Up," *Houston Post*, March 28, 1963.
107  "Unusual Dome Awaits Baseball Season in Houston," *Civil Engineering – ASCE*,
     January 1965.
108  Structural design below Lamella roof structure: Ken Zimmerman, interview by
     Barry Moore, ca. 1994.
109  S.I. Morris, "General Information About the Harris County Sports Stadium,"
     *The Slide Rule* (Official Publication of the Houston Engineering and Scientific
     Society), Vol. 23, No. 5, May 1963.
110  Dene Hofheinz Anton, interview by the author, Houston, February 9, 2014.
111  Fred Hofheinz, interview by the author, Houston, August 30, 2013.
112  "Domed Stadium Free of Support Towers," *Houston Post*, March 13, 1964.
113  Doubts about indoor baseball: John Wilson, "'Dome' Rain Came Day Too Late,"
     *Houston Chronicle*, February 10, 1965, 2, section 7; Dick Peebles, "Astros, Yankees
     Open Fabulous Dome Friday Night," *Houston Chronicle*, April 4, 1965, 13.

114 Roebuck hitting roof: "Stadium Roof Not Hit Proof," *Houston Chronicle*, September 15, 1964; *Inside The Astrodome*, 42-43.
115 Leroy (Satchel) Paige, "Satch Paige Tosses a Few Under the Dome," *Houston Chronicle*, April 4, 1965; *Inside The Astrodome*, 42.
116 "The Judge's Quarters," *Houston Chronicle Texas Magazine*, May 4, 1980.
117 Larry Dierker, interview by Joseph Pratt, July 14, 2008. Houston Oral History Project, Houston Public Library.
118 Mickey Herskowitz, "Fielders Find Dome Flies Hard to Follow." *Houston Post*, April 8, 1965.
119 Herskowitz, "Fielders Find Dome Flies Hard to Follow."
120 "Indoor Arena Excellent For Night Games," *Houston Chronicle*, April 8, 1965.
121 Rebecca Trounson, "Expanding Astrodome Will Bury Some Traditions," *Houston Chronicle*. July 26, 1987.
122 Wells Twombly and Jerry Zuber, "Architect Says He Warned HSA of Glare in Dome," and "Test Color in Glare Saturday," *Houston Chronicle*, April 9, 1965 (Final and Night Final editions), 1. The content of this story was essentially the same in both editions, but the provocative headline was changed at some point during the day.
123 "Test Color in Glare Saturday," *Houston Chronicle*.
124 "Attention Astros! Orange Balls on Way," *Houston Chronicle*, April 9, 1965, Section 6, 6.
125 "'Get It in Writing' on Domed Stadium," *Houston Chronicle*, March 22,1964.
126 I.A. Naman, interview by Barry Moore, ca. 1994, and by the author, August 30, 2013.
127 Traffic control: "No Traffic Jams at Dome," *Houston Chronicle*, April 8, 1965.
128 Beverly Maurice, "Stadium Employees Costumed Like an Operetta – 'At Home' in the Dome" *Houston Chronicle* April 4, 1965.
129 Tal Smith, interview by the author, Sugar Land, TX, May 17, 2013.
130 Betty Ewing, "Grissom Meets another 'Spaceman' in Big Dome," *Houston Chronicle*, April 10, 1965.
131 Beverly Maurice, "Silks, Linens and Hats At Fashionable Game," *Houston Chronicle*, April 10, 1965, 12.
132 Giles, *Pouring Six Beers at a Time*, 44; Cole, *No Color Is My Kind*, Kindle location 1436.
133 Maurice, "Stadium Employees Costumed Like an Operetta."
134 Ibid.
135 "$2 Million Scoreboard Greatest Display of Lights in the World," *Houston Chronicle*, April 8, 1965.
136 Butwin, David, "An Unbelievagable Boom," *Sports Illustrated*, September 4, 1972.
137 Butwin, "An Unbelievagable Boom."
138 Joe Jares, "The Big Screen Is Watching," *Sports Illustrated*, May 31, 1965.
139 Giles, *Pouring Six Beers at a Time*, 68.
140 Press Box amenities: "Writer's Loftiest Praise: Dome Outmodes the Clothes Pin," *Houston Post*, April 26, 1965.
141 Joseph T. Siff, interview by the author, September 3, 2013.
142 County contingency funds: "$1 Million Should Move Ducts, Too," *Houston Chronicle*, April 15, 19 64.
143 Hofheinz emphasized blue: Ann Minick Criswell, "First Photos of Domed Stadium Club Rooms," *Houston Chronicle*, January 10, 1965; and "Designers Kept the Gals in Mind," *Houston Chronicle Texas Magazine*, April 4, 1965.
144 Fred Hofheinz, interview by the author, August 30, 2013.

145   Wells Twombly, "A Matter of Details," *Houston Chronicle*, February 5, 1965; and "Under the Dome," *Houston Post*, February 14, 1965.

146   "the emperor and all the bigwigs sat at the top": Tex Maule, "The Greatest Showman On Earth, And He's The First To Admit It," *Sports Illustrated*, April 21, 1969; and "How We Got Here – Chapter 2: Home In The Dome," *Sports Illustrated*, August 16, 1994.

147   Hofheinz office details: Harold Scarlett, "Goldphone," *Houston Post Sunday Magazine*, June 13, 1965; Hofheinz Estate Auction Offers a Spectrum," *Houston Chronicle*, February 19, 1984; "The Boy Wonder Grows Up," *Houston Chronicle Texas Magazine*, April 4, 1965; Joseph T. Siff interview, September 3, 2013; "bought 26,000 pounds of junk:" Red Smith, "It's Cheaper at Dome Than Staying Home," *Houston Post*, February 15, 1965.

148   Maxine Messenger, "Big City Beat by Maxine," *Houston Chronicle*, April 10, 1965.

149   "President Has Praise for New Stadium," *Houston Chronicle*, April 10, 1965, 7.

150   "Small Flaw in Houston's Diamond," *Business Week*, April 17, 1965.

151   Archie Whitfield, "Sports Slants," *Tyler Courier-Times*-Telegraph, April 11, 1965.

152   Ray, *The Grand Huckster*, 334.

153   "Astros Were Ready With Refunds If Day Games Turned To Comedy," Associated Press story published in *Miami News*, April 12, 1965; Dick Peebles, "Difficult Tasks," *Houston Chronicle*, April 12, 1965.

154   Powell and Wynn quotes: Mickey Herskowitz, "Powell Shellshocked," *Houston Post*, April 11, 1965.

155   Dick Peebles, "Difficult Tasks," *Houston Chronicle*, April 12, 1965.

156   Ralph Anderson, letter to Dr. Chester H. Pheiffer, April 27, 1965; Minchew, 94-274-10.

157   DuPont Working to Overcome Dome Glare," *Houston Chronicle*, April 14, 1965.

158   Suggestions from public: Gary Cartwright, "Astrodome in Trouble," *Houston Post*, April 11, 1965; Wells Twombly, "Help Save The Dome," *Houston Chronicle*, April 15, 1965.

159   Archie Winfield, "Sports Slants," *Tyler Courier-Times* April 11, 1965

160   Twombly, "Help Save The Dome."

161   Mickey Herskowitz, "Astros Grounded 5-2," *Houston Post*, May 24, 1965.

162   "Richards Urges More Painting," *Houston Chronicle*, May 24, 1965.

163   Tracking fly balls against roof structure: "Richards Urges More Painting;" Roy Hofheinz, letter to Mr. Miller, July 13, 1965. Kirksey, Box 8.

164   Hofheinz statements about paint on roof: Robert Heard, "700 Gallons of Paint to Cover Glaring Error," *Galveston News Tribune*, April 20, 1965; "Dome Windows Will be Painted Over," Pasadena, Texas *News Citizen*, April 20, 1965.

165   Ralph Anderson, letter to Dr. Chester H. Pheiffer, April 27, 1965; Minchew, 94-274-10.

166   Rebecca Trounson, "Expanding Astrodome Will Bury Some Traditions" *Houston Chronicle*, July 26, 1987.

167   Barbara Smith Armstrong, telephone interview by the author, October 29, 2013.

168   "Dome 'Breeze' Not Significant, Expert Reports," *Houston Post*, May 10, 1965.

169   Jares, "The Big Screen Is Watching."

170   Dave Anderson, "Finney Goes to Bat for Shea Dome," *New York Journal-American*, May 15, 1965, 16.

171   Boston domed stadium proposal: Will McDonough, "Hub to Get Look at New Stadium" *Boston Globe*, June 16, 1965; Walter Manset, "Boston Eyes Retractable Roof," *Houston Chronicle*, July 11, 1965; Francis Rosa, "Red Sox Back Hub Stadium," *Boston Globe*, May 25, 1966.

172  Buckminster Fuller, letter to Walter O'Malley, September 7, 1965, and Walter O'Malley, postcard to Fuller, September 23, 1965. walteromalley.com, accessed March 30, 2013.

173  Site visitors during construction: Al Jensen, interview by Barry Moore, 1994, Barry Moore Collection; "Job Meeting No. 30, Harris County Domed Stadium 16 October 1963," Elliott Box 1446, Folder 04; Associated Press, "Domed Stadium Is Off Limits," *Amarillo Globe Times*, January 5, 1965.

174  Ernest Bailey, "Hofheinz Asks Court for Dome Tour Funds Ruling" *Houston Post*, September 18, 1969.

175  "Small Flaw in Houston's Diamond," *Business Week*, April 17, 1965.

176  "Annual Boy Scout Circus To Be in Dome on May 8," *Houston Post*, April 8 1965, Sports Section, 6.

177  Accounts of the Boy Scout Circus are drawn from newspaper accounts that appeared in the May 9, 1965, *Houston Post* and *Houston Chronicle*.

178  "Judge is Dreaming About Series," *Brazosport Facts*, April 29, 1965; Ray, *The Grand Huckster*, 335.

179  Staging Aida: Houston Sports Association, *Inside The Astrodome*, 1965, 68.

180  Jack Gallagher, "The Judge – Persuasive Hofheinz Made Dome Dream a Reality" *Houston Post*, May 27, 1979.

181  Wells Twombly, "Hofheinz Denies Contract Would Have Bled Oilers," *Houston Chronicle*, June 10, 1965.

182  Nealon, et al., "Campaign for Baseball," 44-45; Ray, *The Grand Huckster*, 286.

183  Wells Twombly, "Astrodome Makes Baseball History, Unique Park Triumph for Dynamic Duo," *The Sporting News*, April 17, 1965.

184  George Pharr, "Man About Sports," undated article ca.1965, Kirksey Box 8.

185  Dick Peebles, "Hofheinz Makes Key Moves for Astro Control," *Houston Chronicle*, July 25, 1965.

186  Mel Young, "Says Hofheinz Is 'Just Too Autocratic,'" *Houston Chronicle*, August 3, 1965.

187  HSA Public Affairs Chief Paul Haney, quoted in Ray, *The Grand Huckster*, 449.

188  Ray, *The Grand Huckster*, 321.

189  Mickey Herskowitz – Interview by Jim Barlow, December 6, 2010. Houston Oral History Project, Houston Public Library.

190  John Wilson, "Kirksey: Man With 'Idea,'" *Houston Chronicle*, May 13, 1966.

191  Roy Hofheinz, letter to George Kirksey, November 8, 1965, Kirksey Papers Box 8.

192  Wilson, "Kirksey: Man With 'Idea;'" "George Kirksey, Father of Majors Here, Out of Scene," *Houston Chronicle*, May 13, 1966.

193  Tal Smith, interview by the author, Sugar Land, TX, May 17, 2013.

194  Ibid.

195  Ibid.

196  Barbara Moran, "Artificial Grass and How it Grew," *Invention & Technology*, Spring 2005

197  Richard Hoffer, "Dr. Harold Gores," *Sports Illustrated*, September 19, 1994.

198  Tal Smith, interview by the author, Sugar Land, TX, May 17, 2013.

199  Fred Hofheinz, interview by the author, August 30, 2013.

200  Moran, "Artificial Grass and How It Grew."

201  Ray, *The Grand Huckster*, 345.

202  Moran, "Artificial Grass and How It Grew."

203  Wells Twombly, "Hall of Wonders," *Houston Chronicle*, March 15, 1966.

204  Ray, *The Grand Huckster*, 346.

205  "Infield in the Astrodome Delivers More Bounce," *The New York Times*, May 29, 1966.

206  Synthetic turf's market share: Mark Armour, "Sometimes a Great Notion: Artificial Surfaces in Baseball," research presented at the national convention of the Society for American Baseball Research, Minneapolis, Minnesota, June 29, 2012. http://sabr.org/convention/sabr42-presentations, accessed February 8, 2013.

207  Dan J. Forrestal, *Faith, Hope & $5,000: The Story of Monsanto* (New York: Simon & Schuster, 1977), 209.

208  "Harper Goff; Film Stage Designer Did Work for Disney," *Los Angeles Times*, March 10, 1993.

209  Richard Conniff, "Farewell To An Odd Dome Home," *Sports Illustrated*, March 14, 1988.

210  Dene Hofheinz Anton, interview by the author, Houston, February 9, 2014.

211  Marge Crumbaker, "Home Home in the Dome," *Tempo*, May 18, 1969.

212  Barbara Smith Armstrong, phone interview by the author, October 29, 2013.

213  Ray, *The Grand Huckster*, 409-10.

214  Ray, *The Grand Huckster*, 409.

215  Ibid.

216  Barbara Smith Armstrong, interview by the author, Houston, April 22, 2013; "Memories, Treasures of Roy Hofheinz Go on The Auction Block," undated clipping ca. 1984. HMRC Hofheinz Flat File.

217  Dene Hofheinz Anton, interview by the author, February 9, 2014.

218  Richard Conniff, "Farewell to an Odd Dome Home," *Sports Illustrated*, March 14, 1988.

219  "Judge Roy Builds His Own Monument," *National Observer*, April 29, 1968.

220  Twombly, "Astrodome Makes Baseball History."

221  "Judge Roy Builds His Own Monument," *National Observer*, April 29, 1968.

222  Norris McWhirter and Ross McWhirter, *Guinness Book of World Records* (New York: Bantam Books, 1977), 252-53.

223  "Is Public Sentiment favoring Hofheinz Now?" *Houston Chronicle*, March 2, 1967.

224  Was not the same man: Tal Smith interview.

225  Nealon et. al., "Campaign for Baseball," page 46.

226  C.W Skipper, "Astrodome Special Feature[s] Hofheinz," *Houston Post*, April 4, 1975.

227  Ray, *The Grand Huckster*, 517.

228  Rosalind Jackler, "Judge Roy Hofheinz," *Houston Post*, November 23, 1982.

229  Background on the 1999 NLDS and Game Four was drawn from baseball-reference.com, http://www.baseball-reference.com/boxes/HOU/HOU199910090.shtml, accessed June 22, 2013. Description of the final play from "Astrodome – Final Pitch," http://www.youtube.com/watch?v=X_q5boVwbSY&feature=player_detailpage, accessed January 13, 2013.

230  "A Barnum Named Hofheinz, A Big Top Called Astrodome," *New York Times*, July 21, 1968.

231  Bill Koenig, "Sterile Astrodome a Necessary Evil in Humid Houston," *Seattle Times*, October 3, 1999.

232  Union Station background: Tom Marsh, "Houston Union Station: The Great Hall Revealed," http://www.kingswayrc.com/gcst/union/union.htm, accessed June 22, 2013.

233  "Astros Will Try to Grow Grass Inside, Again," Associated Press story in *Lubbock Avalanche-Journal*, February 7, 2000.

234  Michael A. Lutz, "AC Turned on at Astros' Enron Field," Associated Press, May 27, 2000. http://www.apnewsarchive.com/2000/AC-Turned-on-at-Astros-Enron-Field/id-ce8780105cdd99d4fddd689362965f97, accessed June 22, 2013.

# ABOUT THE AUTHOR

JAMES GAST is a registered architect specializing in large-scale public infrastructure projects. A former Houston resident, he has more than 30 years of major project experience in Texas and throughout North America. He holds a Bachelor of Architecture degree from Cornell University.

Made in the USA
Monee, IL
16 December 2020

53392403R20115